Personal Best

Workbook

B2 Upper Intermediate

Series Editor
Jim Scrivener

Authors
Elizabeth Walter
and **Kate Woodford**

1	Your unique style	p2
2	Culture vultures	p8
3	A sense of place	p14
4	Mind and behaviour	p20
5	Our planet	p26
6	Habits and change	p32
7	Lifelong learning	p38
8	The changing media	p44
9	The power of design	p50
10	The business world	p56
11	Fact and fiction	p62
12	New discoveries	p68
	WRITING PRACTICE	p74

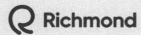

UNIT 1

Your unique style

1A LANGUAGE

GRAMMAR: Present forms; *like*, *as if*, and *as though*

1 Complete the sentences with the words in the box. There are two you do not need.

> know   am knowing   thinks   's thinking   play
> are playing   feels   's feeling   have   are having

1 Felipa _____ worried at the moment because her dad is ill.
2 Gabriel _____ that classical music is boring.
3 We _____ some problems at work at the moment.
4 It's a difficult question but I _____ the answer.
5 Renata may come to the cinema with us. She _____ about it.
6 It _____ as though it's getting colder.
7 At the weekends they _____ volleyball on the beach.
8 My grandparents _____ more than thirty grandchildren now.

2 Use the prompts to complete the sentences with the present simple or present continuous.

1 Lucia says that Daniel isn't speaking to Pablo.
_____
(sound / as if / he / be / angry about something)
2 Hi, Julieta. Good to see you!
_____?
(where / you / work / at the moment)
3 Don't touch that laptop. It
_____.
(belong to / Victoria)
4 My granddad has a smartphone but
_____.
(he / not understand / how to use it)
5 What is that vegetable? It
_____.
(look / a bit like cabbage)
6 My brother plays the piano really well. He
_____.
(practise / for three hours / every day)
7 _____ and it's annoying because she never asks.
(Mia / always / use / my pens)
8 _____ because she has a new job in Chicago.
(Rafaela / learn English)

VOCABULARY: Body language and communication

3 Match sentences 1–6 with a–f.

1 Alejandro had to raise his voice. _____
2 Pablo frowned. _____
3 Matias gazed at the painting. _____
4 Diego winked at me. _____
5 Juan Pablo stared at the photo. _____
6 Emmanuel waved at me. _____

a It was absolutely beautiful.
b He knew I would find the situation funny, too.
c He wanted to get my attention.
d It was very noisy in the room.
e He was shocked at what it showed.
f The letter contained news he did not want to hear.

4 Complete the missing words in the sentences.

1 When I arrived at the party, he k_____ me on the cheek.
2 He introduced me to his friends and we all s_____ hands.
3 When I asked her if she spoke English, she n_____.
4 When I asked him if he had broken the window, he s_____ his head.
5 She looked very unhappy and refused to make eye c_____ with me.
6 The old man just s_____ his shoulders when she asked him if there was a hotel nearby.
7 As I was leaving the train, someone t_____ me on the shoulder.
8 When he met his daughter at the airport, he gave her a big h_____.

PRONUNCIATION: /ə/

5 ▶1.1 Read the sentences aloud. Pay attention to the /ə/ sound in *as*. Listen and repeat.

1 It looks as if we've missed the bus.
2 Tom sounds as though he's disappointed.
3 Do you feel as if we're being unfair?
4 I feel as though I'm in a dream.
5 Those animals look as if they're hungry.
6 It sounds as if you need some help.

SKILLS 1B

LISTENING: Identifying attitude

1 ▶1.2 Listen to a conversation between Sophia and her friend Joe. Are the following statements true (T) or false (F)?

1 Sophia reminds Joe that Elon Musk recently put a sports car in space. _____
2 At first, Joe says that putting a car in space was a good thing to do. _____
3 Sophia says that the car in space was Elon Musk's biggest achievement. _____
4 Sophia says that Elon Musk's company will help the human race. _____
5 Joe suggests that exploring space is bad for the environment. _____
6 Sophia believes that people will not always be able to live on Earth. _____
7 Sophia says that environmental scientists don't have a good opinion of Elon Musk. _____
8 In the end, Joe still doesn't agree with Sophia that Elon Musk is cool. _____

2 ▶1.2 Listen again. Focus on the way Sophia and Joe use words and phrases to say how certain their opinions are or how much they agree with each other. Complete the sentences.

1 These are products that will have far-reaching benefits for the whole of humankind! I _____ that.
2 Joe: That's not very green, is it?
   Sophia: Oh, no, it _____ can be!
3 ... if Earth is destroyed, people can go and live there. I _____ that this will happen one way or another.
4 I _____ that anyone with *that* much money who does *good* things with it is cool.
5 It's better than hanging out on yachts _____!

3 ▶1.3 Look at the sentences. Use the mark ‿ to show where consonant sounds between two words have merged. The first one is done for you. Listen, check and repeat.

1 I just‿can't imagine living like that.
2 Nick calmly handed her the papers.
3 He's the fattest dog I've ever seen.
4 I don't expect to see him there.
5 She said that she was leaving.
6 Tom was sitting at the next table.

4 Complete the compound adjectives in the sentences with the words in the box.

| thinking moving famous minded changing |
| aged respected looking |

1 Her parents were both good-_____, so it's no surprise that she's attractive.
2 It's only forward-_____ businesses like these that will survive going into the future.
3 She was one of the most highly-_____ lawyers of her generation.
4 He was middle-_____ – I'm guessing about fifty.
5 The article featured the diets of ten world-_____ athletes.
6 In such a large organisation, changes are slow-_____ and that can be frustrating.
7 Winning a sum of money as large as that would be completely life-_____.
8 I like to think that I'm open-_____ and willing to change my opinions about things.

3

1C LANGUAGE

GRAMMAR: Narrative tenses

1 Choose the correct options to complete the sentences.

1 I wanted to tell them my news, but I _____ for the right moment.
 a waited   b was waiting   c had waited
2 I knew she was disappointed with her exam results and I could see that she _____.
 a cried   b had cried   c had been crying
3 Luisa was surprised when I _____ her the letter.
 a showed   b was showing   c had showed
4 He went online and _____ a ticket for the show.
 a booked   b had booked   c had been booking
5 I had no idea that Jack _____ to China before.
 a was going   b had been   c had been going
6 We realized that she _____ for months to protect her friend.
 a lied   b was lying   c had been lying
7 When I went to get my passport out, I realized that I _____ it.
 a lost   b had lost   c had been losing
8 I _____ a bath when someone rang the bell.
 a had   b was having   c had had

2 Complete the story with the correct form of the verbs in brackets.

Last Saturday, I [1]_____ (go) with a group of friends to our friend David's flat. It was his birthday, and we [2]_____ (want) to organize a surprise party. He wasn't there because he [3]_____ (play) football, as he always did on Saturday evenings. However, his mum [4]_____ (give) us a key to his flat, so we went in and [5]_____ (get) everything ready for the party. There was so much food – we [6]_____ (prepare) it all day! When David came home he was so shocked – he [7]_____ (not have) any idea about our plans. There was lots of music and dancing, and we [8]_____ (have) a great time when we suddenly noticed that David [9]_____ (fall) asleep. He [10]_____ (run) around so much at his football practice, he was exhausted!

VOCABULARY: Expectations

3 Complete the sentences with the verbs in the box.

| fail   be   make   get   lower   meet |

1 Unfortunately, the hotel didn't _____ our expectations.
2 This café is just what the area needs. I'm sure it will _____ a success.
3 These flowers are for my new boyfriend's mum. I want to _____ a good first impression!
4 Flats are really expensive here. You may have to _____ your expectations.
5 With a fantastic performance like that, you can't _____ to win the competition!
6 If you don't take this opportunity, you won't _____ a second chance.

4 Complete the second sentence to mean the same as the first. Use a noun or a verb from the same family as the underlined word.

1 My parents are very proud of me so I don't want to disappoint them.
 I don't want to be _____ to my parents because they're very proud of me.
2 I met my brother's new girlfriend and she made a good impression on me.
 My brother's new girlfriend really _____ when we met.
3 If the business succeeds, we'll all become rich.
 We'll all become rich if the business is _____.
4 What expectations did you have when you took the job?
 What _____ when you took the job?
5 He was very upset when he failed to get into the team.
 He was very upset by _____ get into the team.
6 I wasn't at all impressed by the hotel.
 The hotel _____ bad _____ on me.

PRONUNCIATION: Stress in narrative tenses

5 ▶1.4 Underline the stressed syllable in the verb in each sentence, then read the sentence aloud. Listen and check.

1 They'd seen the man somewhere before.
2 The children were jumping up and down.
3 The police had been searching for evidence.
4 She had given him all the relevant documents.
5 We'd been expecting her to call.
6 My mother was planning to quit her job.

SKILLS 1D

WRITING: Making a narrative interesting

An unexpected HOBBY

1. About this time last year, my manager said, 'You look exhausted, Simon. Why don't you take a holiday?' It was true that I had been working very hard and, when I looked in the mirror, I could see what she meant. The skin around my eyes was so dark that I looked like a panda. I hadn't slept properly for weeks.

2. I decided to go on a skiing trip with some friends. I thought the exercise and mountain air would be good for me. On the way, I looked out of the window of the plane at the snow sparkling like diamonds on the mountains below. Before long, I was feeling more relaxed than I had done in months, and I couldn't wait to get my skis on.

3. However, when we eventually arrived at the resort, we had a huge shock. 'I'm sorry,' the receptionist at our hotel said, 'but the only snow is at the top of the mountains. And I'm afraid the ski lifts are closed because of strong winds.' Lying in bed that night, I could feel my disappointment like a black cloud over my head.

4. At first, I was sure the holiday would be a disaster. However, the following morning I noticed a sign in the hotel advertising salsa classes. I was nervous because I'd never danced before, but when I anxiously opened the door the teacher called, 'Come on in, you'll love it!' In a matter of minutes, I'd learned some basic steps, and the loud rhythms of the music immediately made me feel more cheerful.

5. After that, I went back every day, even after it snowed more and I was able to go skiing. As time went on, I realized I had found an activity I absolutely loved. When I got home, I found a local class and I've been doing it twice a week ever since.

1 Read Simon's blog post about a holiday that didn't turn out as expected. According to the post, are the sentences below true (T) or false (F)?

1. Simon didn't want to go on holiday, but his boss made him go.
2. He was excited about going skiing.
3. He was surprised to discover that he wouldn't be able to ski.
4. He knew he would enjoy salsa dancing.

2 Which paragraphs include the following?

1. a prediction or comment about the future
2. an interesting comparison
3. direct speech

3 Complete the paragraph with the time linkers in the box or in Simon's post. There may be more than one answer, but do not use the same linker twice.

| to begin with | in a matter of minutes |
| after a while | eventually | in no time |

We set off up the mountain path, expecting to reach the top by midday. ¹_____, everyone was cheerful and we made good progress but we hadn't got very far when the weather changed and it started to get cold and foggy. ²_____ the fog was as thick as soup and we could hardly see anything. We continued on our way, but ³_____ we became less and less enthusiastic about the climb. There didn't seem much point if we couldn't see anything from the top. However, when we ⁴_____ reached the top of the mountain, the fog suddenly disappeared. The view was like a picture postcard, and ⁵_____ everyone was happy again.

4 Write a blog post about an experience that didn't turn out as you had expected.

- Include different narrative tenses and time linkers.
- Use comparisons, predictions and direct speech to make your story more interesting.

5

1 REVIEW and PRACTICE

HOME   BLOG   **PODCASTS**   ABOUT   CONTACT

Tom and Sam talk about handshakes.

LISTENING

1 ▶ 1.5 Listen to the podcast and number a–f in the order that you hear them (1–6).

a smiling when you shake someone's hand ____
b an article Sam read on handshakes ____
c the two-handed handshake ____
d Tom saying that Sam shook his hand ____
e how hard you should squeeze the other person's hand ____
f the peaceful origin of the handshake ____

2 ▶ 1.5 Listen again and choose the correct options.

1 Sam is thinking about handshakes because
   a she has recently written an article about shaking hands.
   b she has recently read an article about shaking hands.
   c she has just shaken Tom's hand.
2 Originally, shaking someone's hand showed that
   a you did not want to hurt them.
   b you knew them.
   c you wanted to work with them.
3 Sam claims that
   a all handshakes are basically the same.
   b there are many different handshakes.
   c there are two different handshakes.
4 The chief executive clearly thought
   a that people should shake hands more.
   b that the way someone shakes hands isn't important.
   c that the way someone shakes hands is very important.
5 Sam says that when you shake someone's hand, you should
   a look at them.
   b smile at them.
   c look at them and smile at them.
6 Tom says he never
   a shakes hands using both hands.
   b presses the other person's hand.
   c shakes hands with anyone.

READING

1 Read Daniel's blog on page 7 and choose the best summary.

a He would like to become a better person generally.
b He would like to make more friends and generally be more sociable.
c He would like to be better at telling jokes.

2 Are the sentences true (T), false (F) or doesn't say (DS)?

1 Daniel blogs regularly on a variety of subjects. ____
2 Daniel shares a home with at least one other person. ____
3 Daniel sometimes goes out with Charlie. ____
4 Charlie is popular because he is good at listening to people. ____
5 Daniel's neighbour was pleased to see him smiling more. ____
6 He tried telling people about his unusual interests. ____
7 He succeeded in listening more than talking at the party the previous night. ____
8 Using people's names more had been a great success. ____
9 He isn't looking forward to the pirate party. ____
10 He hasn't prepared for the pirate party. ____

REVIEW and PRACTICE 1

HOME **BLOG** PODCASTS ABOUT CONTACT

Being a bit more like Charlie

My flatmate, Charlie, is the most sociable person I've ever met. He has – I'm not joking – more friends than he can count. Walk down a street with him and people wave and shout his name. Sit down in a café with him and an old friend will tap him on the shoulder. I've always been – I'm not going to lie – a *bit* jealous of Charlie with his army of friends.

As some of you know, my new year's resolution was to try and widen my circle of friends. Determined to be a bit more like Charlie, I found a website about self-improvement last week and came up with the following five-point action plan for myself:

1 Smile and make eye contact to establish that you're both friendly and confident.
2 Be yourself. Tell people about your unusual interests and experiences! Apparently, what makes you different makes you interesting!
3 Listen. Forgotten all your funny stories? Can't think of anything to contribute to the conversation? Relax! Listen and let the other person do the talking.
4 Use people's names (even though it feels strange). People feel special when you say their names.
5 Accept invitations even though you'd much rather stay at home.

So how am I doing? Mm ... I'll let you be the judge:

1 This has been a struggle. It must be said, I'm not by nature a smiler. Two days into my 'be a bit more like Charlie' project, my neighbour asked me what the joke was. I explained there was no joke and that I was just pleased to see her. She looked a little uncomfortable and cut short the conversation. That said, I've had two very enjoyable, smiley chats with strangers (friends of friends). One of them even resulted in a party invitation – result! (See no. 5 below.)
2 Bit of a disappointment, this one. It turns out *nobody* wants to know about my love of old maps.
3 Interesting ... I went to a party last night feeling tired (I'd been studying all day) but instead of desperately trying to think of entertaining stories, I *listened*. To begin with, it felt strange. Would people think I was shy or, worse, boring? But, as the evening went on, I started to relax and actually *enjoy* the experience.
4 Note to self: people don't feel *special* when you get their names wrong. Enough said.
5 That invitation was to a *pirate-themed* party this Saturday. Not my usual thing – it sounds a bit like a nightmare to be honest – but I'm going! And, yes, I've got the hat and the (toy) parrot.

So, a mixed experience in all but I feel as if I should continue. Will let you know how Week 2 goes ...

UNIT 2 Culture vultures

2A LANGUAGE

GRAMMAR: Question patterns

1 Choose the correct words to complete the sentences. There are two you do not need.

| won't | wasn't | hasn't | didn't | aren't |
| weren't | haven't | doesn't | isn't | don't |

1 _____ your uncle got a sports car?
2 Do you know why Joe _____ go to the party?
3 Your brother's a great cook, _____ he?
4 Why _____ the doors locked last night?
5 Samuel will give us a lift, _____ he?
6 Can you explain why you _____ done your homework?
7 Why are you here? _____ you usually play tennis on Fridays?
8 They _____ expecting us to pay them, are they?

2 Use *wh-* subject or object questions, negative questions, tag questions or indirect questions to complete the questions in the conversation. For questions that need verbs, use the verbs in brackets.

Ava	Hi Brad! I didn't expect to see you today. What ¹_____ (you, do) here?
Brad	I came to see Simon. Do you have any idea where ²_____ (he, be)?
Ava	Yes, he's in his office upstairs, but I don't think you should interrupt him. He's very busy. He said he has over 100 emails to answer.
Brad	That's a lot! I guess he gets a lot of letters, too. Who ³_____ (deal) with them?
Ava	Nobody – he does everything himself.
Brad	Really? ⁴_____ (he, not have) a secretary?
Ava	No, it's ridiculous, ⁵_____? Anyway, what ⁶_____ (you, want) to speak to him about? Is it anything I can help with?
Brad	I was hoping he could help me move some furniture at the weekend. But if he's so busy, I'd better not ask.
Ava	Oh, well my son Diego's a big strong boy. Why ⁷_____ (you, not ask) him instead? I'll give you his number.
Brad	That's great, thanks! ⁸_____ (you, know) if he's free on Saturday morning?
Ava	Hmm. Well he doesn't usually get up until lunch time. Teenagers are always like that, ⁹_____?
Brad	I know. What ¹⁰_____ (make) them so tired all the time?

VOCABULARY: Adjective suffixes

3 Add suffixes from the box to complete the words.

| -ful | -al | -able | -ous | -ive | -less |

1 These snakes are completely harm_____.
2 Our trip to New York was really memor_____.
3 I had a dread_____ journey – our train was very late.
4 He's very convention_____ – he always wears a tie.
5 She enjoys adventur_____ sports like rock climbing.
6 They've got a very aggress_____ dog.

4 Complete the adjectives.

1 A c_____ person thinks carefully before they do anything and doesn't take risks.
2 A u_____ tool helps you to do or make something.
3 A_____ damage is damage that nobody intended to happen.
4 A h_____ person doesn't have a home.
5 An e_____ treatment for an illness is one that works very well.
6 If your feet are p_____, they hurt.
7 If an activity is o_____, you can choose whether to do it or not.
8 Someone who is a_____ wants to have a successful career.
9 If an object is d_____, a lot of people want to have it.
10 If you take decisions fast, you're d_____.

PRONUNCIATION: Intonation in tag questions

5 ▶ 2.1 Listen to the sentences and decide whether the speaker is asking a real question in order to check something or is making a comment. Then listen again and repeat.

		Question	Comment
1	Daniel enjoyed the museum, didn't he?		
2	These paintings are beautiful, aren't they?		
3	You don't like opera, do you?		
4	Your brother lives in Lima, doesn't he?		
5	Teresa is very strict with her children, isn't she?		
6	He's on holiday, isn't he?		

8

SKILLS 2B

READING: Skimming and scanning

A. Have you ever tried to be more like a character in a novel? Perhaps you started using a phrase of theirs or bought clothes to look more like them. If this describes you, you are not alone! Research suggests that readers of novels sometimes start behaving – and even thinking – like the fictional characters in their favourite books. Some may even start believing what the characters believe. It seems that what we read can have a huge effect on us.

B. Other studies on the effects of reading found that many readers could actually 'hear' what the characters on the page were saying. Characters had an actual 'voice'. For some readers, that voice wasn't silenced when the book was put down. A reader might be choosing a dish in a restaurant and find themselves wondering what a character from a favourite novel might order. Indeed, some readers even reported having regular conversations in their heads with characters, as if they had a real-life relationship with them. Others said that once a novel was finished, they found themselves 'missing' a character, just as they would miss a departed friend or lover.

C. Interestingly, it seems that what people experience when reading isn't quite the same as their experience when watching a film. People watching a film might react emotionally to what they see, but they remain aware that they are watching someone else. People reading a story lose their sense of 'separateness' and personally feel what the character feels. What we read, then, has a powerful effect on the human mind.

D. So what is it about the written word that makes characters live and breathe for us? Why do we feel this unique connection with people in books? The answer might lie in the brain's reaction. What scientists have recently discovered is that reading causes activity in many more areas of the brain than previously thought. You would expect that the words 'lemon,' 'roses' and 'perfume' would cause activity in the language-processing parts of your brain. However, it seems they also excite the areas in the brain related to smells. In other words, reading about an experience is more like actually having that experience than we thought before.

1 Skim the text quickly. Match paragraphs A–D with summaries 1–4.

1 How fictional characters can seem real to some readers. _____
2 The part that the brain plays in the reading experience. _____
3 How the characters in books can sometimes influence the behaviour of readers. _____
4 The difference between people's reactions to novels and films. _____

2 Read the questions and underline the key words. Then choose the correct answers.

1 What did studies show about people who read novels?
   a They are rarely influenced by the behaviour of the people in the novels they are reading.
   b They sometimes change their behaviour to be more like the people in the novels they are reading.
   c They like reading novels in which the characters have the same beliefs as them.
2 What did some readers report about the 'voice' of a fictional character?
   a It was similar to their own.
   b They could hear it sometimes when they weren't reading.
   c They sometimes used it, for example to order food in a restaurant.
3 When they are watching movies, people …
   a never forget that the action is happening to someone else.
   b do not experience the emotions that the characters feel.
   c feel as if the action is happening to them personally.
4 Which parts of the brain are affected by words like 'lemon' and 'roses'?
   a the parts that deal with language
   b the parts that are concerned with smell
   c the parts that are concerned with language and smell

3 Complete the second sentence so that it means the same as the first using clauses with *what*. The first one is done for you.

1 I liked the dress that she wore for the Oscars ceremony.
   I liked *what she wore* for the Oscars ceremony.
2 The food that we eat can have a massive effect on our health.
   _____ can have a massive effect on our health.
3 I still can't believe the things that she told me last night!
   I still can't believe _____!
4 I gave him the money I had in my pocket.
   I gave him _____.
5 The things that I saw that night will stay with me forever.
   _____ will stay with me forever.

9

2C LANGUAGE

GRAMMAR: Using linkers (1)

1 Choose the correct options to complete the sentences.

1 I went to the baker's _____ buy some bread.
   a to   b so that   c despite

2 He went to work _____ the fact that he had a bad cold.
   a even though   b although   c in spite of

3 She took a bottle of water _____ she wouldn't be thirsty on the journey.
   a in order to   b to   c so that

4 I arranged to meet Luciana at the station. _____, she didn't come.
   a Despite   b However   c Though

5 The film wasn't what I was expecting. I enjoyed it, _____.
   a however   b despite   c though

6 _____ I've lived in Mexico City for years, I've never visited the pyramids.
   a Even though   b Despite   c However

7 We had a pleasant walk _____ the weather wasn't very nice.
   a in spite of   b although   c however

8 _____ our thick coats, we were still cold.
   a Even though   b Despite   c Although

2 Are these sentences correct or incorrect? Remember to check the punctuation as well as the words. Rewrite the incorrect sentences.

1 There was a lot of work to do however we managed to finish it all.
   _____

2 Despite not going to school, she is very well-educated.
   _____

3 He got a job in order to saving money for his holiday.
   _____

4 I called Samuel for to invite him to dinner.
   _____

5 She always travels first class, despite the fact that it costs a lot.
   _____

6 We took the food with us in order to not waste it.
   _____

7 I sat near the stage so that see the play better.
   _____

8 She passed all her exams, despite not study very much.
   _____

VOCABULARY: Phrasal verbs (1)

3 Match the two parts of the sentences.

1 We had to do without   a her mother.
2 Amy really takes after   b the meeting.
3 The tickets sold out   c his older brother.
4 I've used up   d hot water for several days.
5 They've had to call off   e that website before.
6 He looks up to   f all the credit on my phone.
7 He decided to turn down   g within two hours.
8 I'd never come across   h the job.

4 Complete the text with the correct form of the phrasal verbs in the box.

> put up with   come up with   give in   turn up
> figure out   talk into   get out of   pay off

I have a Saturday job in a bike shop. I love it, but last year my boss's son started working there, too. It didn't take me long to ¹_____ that he wasn't interested in bikes at all – only the money he was earning. He usually ²_____ late to the shop and even then he would try to ³_____ actually doing anything useful. I ⁴_____ it for a few weeks, but I was getting more and more fed up.

In the end, I ⁵_____ an idea. I persuaded his dad to pay us according to how many bikes we sold. He agreed, and my plan soon ⁶_____. I was earning more, and his son was earning much, much less. After a few more weeks he ⁷_____ and admitted that the bike shop wasn't for him. Then I managed to ⁸_____ my best friend _____ applying for his job, and he got it, so now things at the shop are perfect!

PRONUNCIATION: Sentence stress

5 ▶2.2 Read the sentences aloud and underline the stressed words in the phrases in **bold**. Listen and check.

1 I borrowed some money from my parents **in order to buy a car**.
2 **In spite of my worries**, the exam was fine.
3 I wore gloves **so that my hands wouldn't get cold**.
4 I'm proud of my work **despite his criticism**.
5 **In order not to upset my parents**, I came home early.
6 **Despite having studied French for five years**, she can't speak it very well.

SKILLS 2D

SPEAKING: Making and responding to recommendations

1 ▶ 2.3 Complete these phrases connected with making and responding to recommendations. Then listen to the conversation between Emma and Alex and check.

1 It's one of the best things I've seen in a _____ time.
2 If you _____ superhero movies, you're going to _____ this.
3 I'm not _____ on superhero movies.
4 My cousin is _____ about movies with lots of action.
5 It's _____ shocking and fascinating at the same time.
6 I don't really _____ like watching that sort of thing at the moment.
7 I'm in the _____ for something more cheerful.
8 It's definitely _____ seeing some time.

2 Look again at the sentences in exercise 1. Which are used for making recommendations (M), and which for responding to recommendations (R)?

1 ___   3 ___   5 ___   7 ___
2 ___   4 ___   6 ___   8 ___

3 ▶ 2.3 Listen again. Give a short answer to each question.

1 What's the movie *Black Panther* about? _____
2 When's it set? _____
3 What did Alex like about it? _____
4 What's the name of the actor who played the king's son? _____
5 What's the name of the writer of *I Tonya*? _____
6 What's *I Tonya* about? _____
7 Does Alex want to watch it? _____

4 Match questions 1–5 with responses a–e.

1 What's it about? ___
2 Why did you like it so much? ___
3 Who's in it? ___
4 When does the story take place? ___
5 Who wrote it? ___

a I think what I loved was the relationship between the characters.
b Roy Scheider plays the police chief and Robert Shaw is the shark hunter.
c It was written by Peter Benchley and Carl Gottlieb.
d It tells the story of some men who want to kill a shark.
e It's set in the 1970s.

5 Complete the dialogue with information about a movie you like.

A	I think I'm going to stay in tonight. Can you recommend a movie?
B	Yes, how about _____?
A	What's it about?
B	_____. If you like _____, you're going to love it.
A	Oh, OK. Who's in it?
B	_____.
A	And when's it set?
B	_____.
A	OK, and what is it that you like about it?
B	_____.
A	Sounds great, thanks!

11

2 REVIEW and PRACTICE

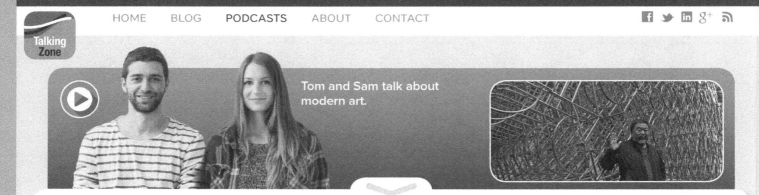

HOME   BLOG   PODCASTS   ABOUT   CONTACT

Tom and Sam talk about modern art.

LISTENING

1 ▶ 2.4 Listen to the podcast. Tick (✓) the things that Tom, Sam and Lucas discuss.
1 The Tate Modern art gallery in London _____
2 how the Tate Modern chooses its exhibitions _____
3 an unusual work of art _____
4 Lucas's favourite museum in Brazil _____
5 how popular modern art is in Brazil _____

2 ▶ 2.4 Listen again. Choose the correct options to complete the sentences.
1 Lucas _____ the art that is always on display in the gallery.
  a disliked
  b enjoyed
  c didn't see
2 Sam tells listeners about an artwork that consists of _____ made of clay.
  a seeds
  b a clay sculpture
  c a sunflower
3 People _____ about Ai Weiwei's work.
  a often disagree
  b sometimes joke
  c usually agree
4 Lucas _____ Ai Weiwei's work in Brazil.
  a has never seen
  b would like to see
  c has seen
5 Lucas admires Ai Weiwei's _____.
  a artistic talent
  b hard work
  c imagination
6 Lucas talks about an art museum that is _____ a botanic garden.
  a near
  b next to
  c in
7 Lucas says that in South America you often see modern art _____.
  a in parks
  b in public places
  c in galleries

READING

1 Read the blog on page 13. Complete 1–5 with the adjectives in the box.

attractive   ridiculous   effective
conventional   ambitious

2 Are the sentences true (T), false (F) or doesn't say (DS)?
1 Eva was still a child when she decided she wanted to become a photographer. _____
2 At the beginning, she had to do a lot of jobs she didn't enjoy. _____
3 The hard work she did at that time was good for her career. _____
4 Nowadays, Eva does not need any help to take great photos. _____
5 Annie Leibovitz knew most of the people she photographed very well. _____
6 Eva admires her photographs of John Lennon and Yoko Ono. _____
7 Eva gets all her information about her subjects by talking to them. _____
8 She has plenty of time to prepare the lighting. _____
9 Eva enjoys photographing her less famous customers more than the very famous ones. _____
10 She gets annoyed with celebrities who want her to make them look better in photos than they do in real life. _____

REVIEW and PRACTICE 2

HOME BLOG PODCASTS ABOUT CONTACT

Guest blogger Eva talks about the art of celebrity photography.

Snapping the stars

Fancy spending your working life mixing with the stars? What better way than to become a celebrity photographer? However, it's not as easy as it looks!

I was only 10 when I first saw a book of photographs by Annie Leibovitz, but from then on I was certain I knew what I wanted to do with my life. I wanted to be a photographer, but not the ¹_____ kind that takes pictures of weddings; I was more ²_____ than that. I wanted to be a celebrity photographer or 'shooter', as they're often called in the business.

Being a shooter is hard work, especially at the beginning when nobody knows you. In the first few years, I worked ³_____ hours and I never turned down a job. At times I was exhausted, but eventually it paid off as I started to get calls from magazine editors and sometimes even from the stars themselves or their agents.

I've been a professional photographer for over 10 years now, and I've been lucky enough to work for some of the best magazines, but I still look up to Annie Leibovitz, and I still study her work so that I can learn how to take the most ⁴_____ shots. When you look at her pictures, it seems as though she was able to see inside the heads of her subjects. She helped me figure out that a photograph needs to show someone's personality, not just what they look like. Look at her pictures of John Lennon and Yoko Ono to see what I mean!

Of course, in order to achieve that, you have to make a connection with the people you're photographing. I always research their lives before I meet them, and I try to keep the conversation going while I'm working, even though that can be difficult when – as is often the case – you only have a few minutes to do your job. Because of that, I always get the lights ready in advance – another thing Annie has taught me is that lighting really is the key to a great photo.

In spite of my best efforts, I know I'll never be as good as her, but I love my job and I've never regretted choosing it. Most of the celebrities I meet are charming – even the very famous ones. The only problem I've had is with people who want me to make them look more ⁵_____ than they really are, but who can blame them when they work in an industry where looks are so important?

UNIT 3 A sense of place

3A LANGUAGE

GRAMMAR: Advice, expectation and obligation

1 Choose the correct options to complete the sentences.

1 It's going to rain today. You *'re supposed to / should / 're allowed to* take an umbrella with you.
2 You *'re not allowed to / 're not supposed to / wouldn't* go swimming after a big meal.
3 If you want to park here, you *have to / should / can* get a ticket from the machine.
4 I need to learn these words because we *shouldn't / 'd better not / can't* use a dictionary in the exam.
5 That dog bites. I *wouldn't / shouldn't / can't* go near it if I were you.
6 My bedroom is such a mess! I *'m allowed to / can / ought to* tidy it up.
7 You *'re not allowed to / 'd better not / wouldn't* travel on this train if you don't have the correct ticket.
8 It's nearly time to go – you *'d better / can / 're supposed to* hurry up!

2 Use the prompts to complete the sentences.

1 You'll probably miss your plane if you go by bus. _____ a taxi.
(better / take)
2 The door is shut. _____ ?
(we / allowed / go in)
3 We started the exercise in class and we _____ it at home.
(supposed / finish)
4 The city centre is dangerous at night. _____ there if I were you.
(wouldn't / go)
5 You look terrible. _____ a doctor.
(ought / see)
6 He's a bit overweight. _____ more exercise.
(should / do)
7 _____ your seatbelt while the car is moving.
(must / wear)
8 Put your camera away. You _____ it in here.
(not allowed / use)

VOCABULARY: Urban places and problems

3 Read the sentences and circle True or False.

1	Places usually look good if there is a lot of vandalism in them.	True	False
2	A harbour is a place where you can park your car.	True	False
3	Smog is a mixture of things like smoke and chemicals that pollute the air.	True	False
4	If there is overcrowding in an area, too many people live there.	True	False
5	It is a good idea to drive your car to places where there is a lack of parking.	True	False
6	Companies often have their offices in the business district of a city.	True	False
7	People who live in poverty are usually quite rich.	True	False
8	In places where there is homelessness, you may see people sleeping in the street.	True	False

4 Complete the sentences.

1 We were late for our meeting because of _____ congestion.
2 We took all the broken equipment to a _____ disposal centre.
3 We had to go to the law _____ to give evidence at her trial.
4 The mayor held a party at the _____ hall.
5 This is the _____ area of the city, where there are lots of factories.
6 Most people here live in _____ buildings with at least 15 floors.
7 There was a huge queue at the taxi _____.
8 The _____ area of a city is the place where most people live.

PRONUNCIATION: /aʊ/, /əʊ/, and /ɔː/

5 ▶ 3.1 Listen to the sentences and tick (✓) the correct column for the underlined vowels. Listen again and repeat.

		/aʊ/	/əʊ/	/ɔː/
1	You're not supp<u>o</u>sed to use a dictionary.			
2	Are we all<u>ow</u>ed to take photos?			
3	He's supp<u>o</u>sed to come home early today.			
4	You really <u>ou</u>ght to eat something.			
5	You're not all<u>ow</u>ed to swim in the lake.			
6	I <u>ou</u>ght to go to the gym later.			

14

SKILLS 3B

LISTENING: Identifying advice

1 ▶ 3.2 Listen to Isabel and Ben's conversation and choose the correct options.

1 Why is Isabel worried about Ben?
   a He isn't sleeping well.
   b He hasn't seen anyone for a while.
   c He looks depressed.

2 What does Isabel say about people generally?
   a They should be happy on their own for long periods.
   b They should always be with other people.
   c They probably shouldn't be alone for long periods.

3 What does Isabel say she did recently?
   a She saw a programme about working from home.
   b She read an article about working from home.
   c She spoke to a friend about working from home.

4 How was the woman who wrote the article affected?
   a She was feeling unhappy.
   b She was sleeping badly.
   c She was feeling unhappy and sleeping badly.

5 What does Isabel suggest that Ben could do?
   a work from her friend's home
   b meet her work colleagues and socialize with them
   c work in a place where there are other people

6 What does Isabel offer to do?
   a put Ben in touch with a friend who might help him
   b give Ben the address of an office where he can work
   c show Ben an office that he can work in

2 ▶ 3.2 Listen again. Focus on the way Isabel gives Ben advice. Complete the sentences.

1 Oh, Ben, _____ spend so much time alone!
2 Yes, but _____ needs company, don't they?
3 _____ supposed to be on our own for days on end.
4 _____ consider renting an office space nearby?
5 You _____ speak to her. I'll give you her mobile number.

3 ▶ 3.3 Listen again. Focus on these negative questions. Mark (R) where the intonation rises because the speaker is checking information. Mark (F) where the intonation falls because the speaker is giving an opinion.

1 Have you really not seen anyone for three days? _____
2 Yes, but everyone needs company, don't they? _____
3 We're social creatures, aren't we? _____
4 People can still suffer if they're working in an office, can't they? _____
5 Yes, but it happens less, doesn't it? _____
6 I should imagine you miss that, don't you? _____

4 Underline the correct word in each sentence.

1 He claimed that 200 people came to hear him speak but the *actual / current* number was closer to 100.
2 I try to *prevent / avoid* eating after eight o'clock in the evening.
3 Stress *effects / affects* different people in different ways.
4 Paolo is a very experienced driver. I always feel *safe / sure* when he's at the wheel.
5 We don't need to make a decision now. We can *discuss / argue* it later.
6 It doesn't *mind / matter* how little I eat, I never seem to lose weight.
7 As I was speaking to Ali, I *realized / noticed* a man at the back of the room wearing a dark suit.
8 I *elected / chose* a black tie because I was going to a funeral.

15

3C LANGUAGE

GRAMMAR: Phrasal verbs

1 Use the prompts to complete the sentences.

1 What time does _____? (off / plane / take / the)
2 I don't know if the dress will fit me. I _____. (to / it / need / on /try)
3 How well do you _____? (your / on / sister / with / get)
4 David _____ for Dad's birthday present. (up / a good / with / idea / came)
5 Oh no! Simon has _____! (up / milk / used / the / all)
6 The head teacher asked me to _____. (visitors / around / school / show / the / some)
7 The lights are too bright. _____, please? (them / off / turn / you / can)
8 Maria's always late for work. I don't know how _____! (away / she / it / gets / with)

2 Rewrite the underlined parts of the sentences with the correct form of the phrasal verbs in the box.

> throw away   take up   come across   turn down
> turn into   take after   look forward to   come back

1 They offered me the job but I said no. _____
2 The children are excited about the party. _____
3 If you want a relaxing hobby, you should start doing yoga. _____
4 My mother made our home become a meeting place for artists. _____
5 The doctor could see you at three, so could you return then, please? _____
6 It's a lovely beach. I was very happy when we found it. _____
7 Luciana is very similar to her aunt. _____
8 These newspapers are really old. You should get rid of them. _____

3 Complete the text with objects from the box, where they are needed. You will not need all of them but you will need one twice. Write ^ where the object should go and write it above the line.

> it   them   the house   that behaviour   my little sister
> an adult   her favourite cookies

Yesterday I had to ¹**look after** while my parents were at work. She's only five, and she can be quite difficult. First, she started screaming because we'd ²**run out of**, so I said we could go to the shop and buy some. While we were ³**looking for**, she noticed an enormous bar of chocolate. I told her she couldn't have it but she ⁴**picked up** anyway and started eating it, so I had to pay for it. Then, when we got outside, she dropped it on the pavement. It was so dirty, we had to ⁵**throw away**, and she started screaming again. And that's how the day went on. I was so pleased when my parents ⁶**came back**. I don't know how they ⁷**put up with** every day. I can't wait for her to ⁸**grow up** and be more fun to spend time with.

PRONUNCIATION: Linking in phrasal verbs

4 ▶3.4 Read the sentences aloud. Pay attention to how the words in the phrasal verbs link together. Listen and repeat.

1 I looked after her apartment while she was away.
2 What time did the plane take off?
3 I saw the dress in a shop and I tried it on.
4 She came up with a great idea for a present.
5 They called off their wedding.
6 I threw out all my old school books.

SKILLS 3D

WRITING: Writing a persuasive article

1 Read the article about Naples and complete 1–6 with a–f.

a At first glance
b However, they are so delicious that nobody needs more choice
c You might think
d but in fact it wasn't particularly cold
e Initially, you get the impression that
f but actually it's a wonderful place to go

2 Find words in the article that are stronger synonyms for the adjectives below.

1 Paragraph 1: nice = _____
2 Paragraph 2: interesting = _____, attractive = _____, good = _____
3 Paragraph 3: tasty = _____
4 Paragraph 4: surprising = _____, big = _____, cold = _____
5 Paragraph 5: good = _____

3 Use your own ideas to complete the sentences by contrasting expectations with reality.

1 You might think that a place this hot would be very dry. However, _____.
2 Initially, you get the impression that the scenery is rather boring, but actually _____.
3 At first glance, the buildings all look the same, but actually _____.
4 You might think that a hotel like this would be really expensive, but in fact _____.
5 At first glance, the coast looks attractive. However, _____.
6 Initially, you get the impression that nothing happens in this town, but actually _____.

4 Think about a place you have enjoyed visiting or a place you would like to go to. Write a text explaining why it is a good place for a holiday.

- State your point of view clearly.
- Give reasons and support them with facts and examples.
- Use persuasive language.
- Include at least two expressions for contrasting expectations with reality.

Naples
City of food and fun!

1 I've just come back from a week in the Italian city of Naples and I'd say it's one of the best places in Europe for a holiday. ¹_____ it's a noisy, rather dirty place where nobody ever relaxes, ²_____.

2 There are so many fascinating places to visit, including castles, palaces and the most exquisite churches you've ever seen. Every corner brings something new, for example incredible fish markets with fish so fresh that many of them are still alive, or tiny shops selling pasta in all shapes, colours and sizes.

3 Of course, Naples is famous for being the home of pizza, and I certainly wasn't disappointed! ³_____, their pizzas may look slightly boring – for example at the famous Pizzeria Michele there are only two types of pizza to choose from, and one of those doesn't even have cheese! ⁴_____.

4 One of the most amazing things about Naples is what goes on underground! We walked down hundreds of steps into an enormous area of rooms and passages under the city. The Romans used it to store clean water, and, during the second world war, the city's citizens hid there to escape from the bombs. ⁵_____ it would be freezing so far down, ⁶_____. You have to be quite slim to squeeze through some of the stone passages, though!

5 If you ask me, Naples is a fantastic place to visit. Just don't go in August, when it's much too hot, and don't even think about trying to drive – the traffic is the craziest I've ever seen!

17

3 REVIEW and PRACTICE

Tom and Sam talk about air pollution in cities.

LISTENING

1 ▶ 3.5 Listen to the podcast. Tick (✓) the statement which is NOT true.

1. In some cities, you are not allowed to drive in particular areas. _____
2. Tom and Sam rarely use their cars. _____
3. Many cities are trying to provide better public transport. _____

2 ▶ 3.5 Listen again and complete the sentences with one or two words.

1. Sam accuses Tom of trying to _____ their guest.
2. Tom tells Sam she'd better _____ her car keys.
3. In Paris at the weekend, cars are not _____ in some areas of the city.
4. In a _____ of the German city of Freiburg, parking near your home is prohibited.
5. In return for not parking near your home, you get a _____ house or apartment.
6. Sam says we all know we _____ to drive less.
7. Many cities are trying to _____ their public transport systems.
8. In the city where Gabriel comes from, there is now no _____ in the air.

READING

1 Read Sylvie's blog on page 19 and choose the best summary.

a. Sylvie thinks Singapore is much better than London.
b. Sylvie thinks London is much better than Singapore.
c. Sylvie is very impressed with Singapore although she also admires London.

2 Tick (✓) the correct sentences.

1. Sylvie knows for sure where she will live in the future. _____
2. London has a number of bad features that all big cities have. _____
3. Sylvie was annoyed that she couldn't chew gum in Singapore. _____
4. Sylvie stayed in the city centre the whole time she was in Singapore. _____
5. Sylvie didn't come across any litter while she was in Singapore. _____
6. Sylvie thinks that all writing or pictures on the walls of public places is bad. _____
7. Singapore doesn't feel like a dangerous city because it is so clean and tidy. _____
8. Sylvie was surprised by the appearance of the trees in Singapore. _____

3 Match the definitions below with six words in Sylvie's blog that are associated with living in cities.

1. when rubbish such as paper, bottles and cans is left lying on the ground in public places
2. the act of damaging things deliberately, especially public property
3. when rude, humorous or political words or drawings are illegally written or drawn on walls or other surfaces
4. when there are not enough places to leave your car
5. when damage is caused to the air or water by harmful substances or waste
6. when there are too many cars on a road

REVIEW and PRACTICE 3

HOME BLOG PODCASTS ABOUT CONTACT

Guest blogger Sylvie writes about her recent trip to Singapore and compares urban living there with London.

A TALE OF TWO CITIES

(Well, OK, one of them is a country ...)

First up, let me say that I love London – I really do. I moved here six years ago to study and if I end up staying in the UK, it'll definitely be in this huge, fascinating city with its 8.8 million inhabitants (and 300+ languages!).

That said, as a 'Londoner', I have to put up with all the usual disadvantages of a capital city – the pollution, the traffic congestion and the lack of parking. (Hey, get rid of the car – that way all three problems are solved!) Usually, I'm so used to these things that I don't even notice them but, after a recent trip to Singapore, I'm perhaps seeing my adopted city a little differently ... For those of you who haven't yet had the opportunity to visit this *astonishing* city-state and island country in South-east Asia, these were a few of the differences that struck me.

It's so *beautifully* clean. Like everyone, I knew that you weren't allowed to carry chewing gum with you in Singapore. (Didn't matter to me – I don't chew the stuff.) What I didn't know before I visited was how *generally* clean it is. I can honestly say that in the seven days that I was there – between the residential area where my friend has her apartment and the business district in the city centre – I didn't see one piece of litter. People are fined or made to clean up if they drop litter so, quite sensibly, they tend not to do it. (I'm not saying this is a good thing or a bad thing, by the way – just making the point that if people know they won't get away with something, they don't do it.)

There's no graffiti on any of the walls. Call it street art or vandalism, depending on your point of view – it simply doesn't exist. In Singapore, you can't write or paint on any public or private building without permission and there are *heavy* fines and even prison sentences for those who break this rule. The combined effect of rubbish-free streets and clean walls is that everywhere looks very attractive and also feels very *safe*. Having said that, by the end of my stay, I was rather missing London's street art. Some of it (not all!) adds a little interest to the urban environment ...

It's so *green*! I don't know why I wasn't expecting this. Yes, London has its street trees and its parks, and very lovely they are, too. But the thing about Singapore's tropical trees is that they are just so ... *green*. And the Gardens by the Bay – a massive nature park – is unlike anything I've ever seen. Perhaps I'll finish with a picture or two ...

UNIT 4 Mind and behaviour

4A LANGUAGE

GRAMMAR: Subject-verb agreement

1 Tick (✓) the sentences that are correct.

1 Everyone was able to come to the party. _____
2 Some of the sandwiches has been eaten. _____
3 The information were very useful. _____
4 Everyone, including you, has to help. _____
5 Several of the plants have died. _____
6 One of the plates are broken. _____
7 Most of the students enjoy her lessons. _____
8 My friends, except for Josh, all has cars. _____

2 Complete the conversation with the present simple or present continuous form of the verbs in brackets.

A Hey, Mia, one of my friends ¹_____ (organize) a picnic this Saturday. Do you want to come?
B Sounds great, but my sister and I ²_____ (go) to the cinema that day. There's a film that both of us really ³_____ (want) to see.
A What time ⁴_____ the film _____ (start)?
B Not until 7.30.
A Well the picnic starts at four, so why ⁵_____ you, and your sister of course, _____ (come) for an hour or two? Oh, by the way, everyone ⁶_____ (bring) some food and drink.
B OK. I love picnics – food always ⁷_____ (taste) better outside! What shall I bring?
A Anything you like. If each person ⁸_____ (bring) something to share, there should be plenty.

VOCABULARY: Personality and behaviour

3 Choose the correct options to complete the sentences.

1 She's so *unreasonable / bossy / responsible* – she's always telling people what to do.
2 Alvin was very *arrogant / stubborn / bad-tempered* today. He shouted at me several times.
3 Our boss wants us to work all this weekend. I think he's being totally *bossy / foolish / unreasonable*.
4 I would definitely trust Becky to babysit. I know she's only 15 but she's very *responsible / stubborn / bossy*.
5 Mia's so *bad-tempered / arrogant / unreasonable*. She thinks she's better than everyone else.
6 Leo let his friend use his credit card. That was a very *foolish / clumsy / responsible* thing to do.
7 Pilar is so *foolish / bad-tempered / stubborn*. It's hard to persuade her to change her mind.
8 Luke is really *clumsy / unreasonable / arrogant* – he's always breaking things.

4 Complete the sentences with the correct form of the verbs in the box. Add prepositions where necessary.

| forgive | get | drive | upset | boast |
| praise | encourage | take (x2) | stand |

1 Yesterday my English teacher _____ me _____ criticizing my accent in front of the whole class. I really don't think that's the best way to _____ students _____ try harder.
2 My brother's always _____ _____ how good he is at football. I have to leave the room when he does that because I just can't _____ it.
3 My cousin persuaded my sister to give him a lot of money even though she doesn't have much herself. I can't _____ him _____ doing that. In my opinion, he _____ advantage _____ her because she's so kind.
4 It _____ _____ my nerves when people drop litter. If I see someone picking it up, I always _____ them _____ it.
5 One of my colleagues is always trying to _____ credit _____ work that I've done. It _____ me crazy!

Pronunciation: *of*

5 ▶ 4.1 Tick (✓) the correct sound for the word *of* in each sentence. Listen, check and repeat.

	/əv/	/ə/
1 My grandparents keep a lot of animals.		
2 Some of our customers are very nice.		
3 Many of my friends still live with their parents.		
4 You need to turn off both of the switches.		
5 I think that's one of Auntie Maria's earrings.		
6 I've already done most of my homework.		

SKILLS 4B

READING: Identifying attitude

WED 13:02

Zoe: Hello, lovely housemates! Just wondering whether anyone else is starting to get a bit ... fed up with Tom's behaviour. 😒

Max: Yup!

Klara: Tell me about it! He woke me up at three o'clock this morning! Tell me if I'm being unreasonable, but I expect people not to make a noise when they get home in the middle of the night. 😠

Javier: I didn't hear a thing.

Max: Javier, nothing wakes you up! For your information, Tom dropped a pan in the kitchen and then tripped and fell while he was coming up the stairs.

Javier: Yeah, he's a bit clumsy sometimes.

Zoe: Personally, I could forgive Tom for coming home late now and then – I'm more annoyed by the fact that he 'borrows' food and never actually replaces it. Twice this week he's finished off my orange juice and not even mentioned it. To my mind, that's completely unacceptable.

Max: Totally agree, Zoe. If you want to upset your housemates, taking food without their permission is a really great way to do it! And he never washes up. I'm always having to wash his dirty plates and mugs. To be honest, I think he takes advantage of us. And, OK, he's very charming and funny, but as far as I'm concerned, that's just not enough.

Javier: Yeah, but no one's actually told him, have they? He probably has no idea that he's doing anything wrong. If I were you, I'd have a word with him. Generally, people are glad if you tell them how they can improve their behaviour.

Klara: Jav, I totally get what you're saying, but Tom is quite sensitive ...

Max: Jav, what planet are you on? People hate it when you criticize them!

Javier: Well, if you don't say anything but carry on being cross with him the whole time, he'll be more upset, that's for sure! While we're on this subject, if you guys came to our monthly house meetings, you could discuss Tom's behaviour with him then. Last time, none of you came – it was just Tom and me. 😟

Klara: That's a good point, Jav. Maybe we should try that.

---

1 Are the following statements true (T) or false (F)?

1. Javier seems less annoyed by Tom's behaviour than his housemates. _____
2. Javier is easily woken up during the night. _____
3. Klara thinks that people who share a house should be quiet late at night. _____
4. What irritates Zoe about Tom is that he takes other people's food. _____
5. Max refuses to do Tom's washing-up for him. _____
6. Max does not accept that Tom has some good qualities. _____
7. Tom's housemates have already told him that he is behaving badly. _____
8. Javier recommends that his housemates speak to Tom about the problem. _____

2 Read the text and decide who has the following opinions. Write K for Klara, M for Max, Z for Zoe and J for Javier.

1. Being noisy at night is not the worst thing Tom does. _____
2. Tom's good qualities do not make his bad behaviour less serious. _____
3. We like it when others suggest how we can be better people. _____
4. Tom is easily upset by other people's comments. _____
5. We don't like it when other people say we are doing something bad. _____

3 Choose the correct options to complete the sentences. Then check your answers in the text.

1. If you want to upset your housemates, taking food without their permission *is / will be* a really great way to do it!
2. If I were you, *I'll / I'd* have a word with him.
3. Generally, people *are / will be* glad if you tell them how they can improve their behaviour.
4. People *hate / will hate* it when you criticize them!
5. Well, if you don't say anything but carry on being cross with him the whole time, *he'll / he'd* be more upset.
6. If you guys *come / came* to our monthly house meetings, you could discuss Tom's behaviour with him then.

21

4C LANGUAGE

GRAMMAR: Perfect and past forms

1 Choose the correct options to complete the sentences.

1 I ___ Daniel at the bus stop this morning.
   a 've seen   b saw   c 've been seeing
2 How long have you ___ the guitar? You're very good.
   a learned   b learn   c been learning
3 I ___ this movie twice already.
   a 've been seeing   b 've seen   c saw
4 She ___ a new laptop last week.
   a 's been buying   b 's bought   c bought
5 He ___ on his book for more than five years and it still isn't finished.
   a 's been working   b worked   c is working
6 I've got lots of homework and I ___ started it yet.
   a haven't been   b didn't   c haven't
7 We haven't started our meal yet because we ___ waiting for Felipe to arrive.
   a been   b have been   c had

2 Find six mistakes in the text. Cross out the mistakes and write the correct version above them.

> I'm going to Australia next summer. I'm very excited, because I never went there before. I've saved up for the trip for over a year now. I want to go to Darwin in the north because I've heard that the scenery is amazing, and I really want to see some crocodiles! I'm also planning to go to Sydney. My dad has lived there for four years when he was younger, and he says it's a great city. I've been doing a lot of research on the internet and I've been finding some great places to stay, including a treehouse in the jungle near Cairns. Yesterday I have received an email from one of my dad's old friends in Sydney, offering me a room there – he knew my dad for over 30 years now, and he's promised to tell me some funny stories about him!

VOCABULARY: Word families

3 Match words 1–8 with definitions a–h.

1 reliable   ___
2 criticism   ___
3 create   ___
4 persuasive   ___
5 achievement   ___
6 risk   ___
7 consider   ___
8 succeed   ___

a able to make people agree with you
b able to be trusted to do something
c something that is dangerous
d something good that you manage to do
e achieve what you want to achieve
f things people say when they think something is bad
g think carefully about something or someone
h make something

4 Complete the second sentence to mean the same as the first. Use a noun, verb or adjective from the same family as the underlined word.

1 She often criticized my work.
   She was often _____ of my work.
2 I'm not certain of David's reliability.
   I'm not sure if we can _____ on David.
3 I wish you wouldn't do so many risky things.
   I wish you wouldn't take so many _____.
4 Do you think it's possible to achieve these goals?
   Do you think these goals are _____?
5 His work is very creative.
   His work shows a lot of _____.
6 Their business was extremely successful.
   Their business was a great _____.

PRONUNCIATION: Sentence stress in perfect forms

5 ▶ 4.2 Listen to the sentences. Underline the stressed words in the phrases in **bold**.

1 **Julieta has done** all her work.
2 Why **have you invited** Tom?
3 **She's been annoying** me all morning!
4 I don't think **they have noticed** the mistake.
5 **Have you been waiting** for a long time?
6 Do you know if **she's bought** a ticket?

SKILLS 4D

SPEAKING: Responding to arguments

1 ▶ 4.3 Listen to Anna telling her friend Paul about something that happened to her. Are the sentences true (T) or false (F)?

1 Anna was angry because the people in the car were driving too fast. ___
2 She put their burger boxes in a bin. ___
3 The people in the car were angry with her. ___
4 Other people thought that what they had done was wrong. ___
5 Anna knew that the police officer was the driver's father. ___
6 The police officer thought his son and his friend had behaved badly. ___

2 ▶ 4.3 Choose the correct options to complete the sentences. Complete the phrases they use. Listen again if you need to.

1 When Paul says that people throw out rubbish because they don't want their car to smell, Anna *agrees / disagrees / asks for clarification*:
I think there's more _____ than that, though.

2 When Anna says that throwing rubbish is a statement about the way people view society, Paul *agrees / disagrees / asks for clarification*:
I'm not sure I _____.

3 When she explains more about what she means, Paul *agrees / disagrees / asks for clarification*:
That makes a lot of _____.

4 When Paul says the police officer is responsible for his son's behaviour, Anna *agrees / disagrees / asks for clarification*:
That may be true to a certain _____.

3 ▶ 4.4 Complete gaps 1–5 in the conversation with phrases a–e. Listen and check.

a I couldn't believe my eyes!
b Let me guess
c No way!
d You're not going to believe what happened last night!
e That must have been so difficult.

A ¹_____ I went to see a band in a bar in town, but when I saw the singer ²_____
B Why?
A It was our old maths teacher, Mrs Hoskins. Do you remember her?
B ³_____ What's she doing singing in a band?
A I wondered that, too. So I went to talk to her in the break.
B ⁴_____ – easier than controlling a class full of naughty kids, right?
A Yes, something like that. And she said that some of the parents were horrible to her and said it was her fault if their kids didn't do well in their exams.
B ⁵_____ Teaching's a tough job, isn't it? I think I'd rather be a singer, too!

4 Look at phrases a–e in exercise 3 again and match them with functions 1–5 below.

1 to describe a reaction ___
2 to show empathy ___
3 to guess how the story will continue ___
4 to create suspense ___
5 to show surprise ___

5 Use your own ideas and phrases you have learned to complete the conversation.

A You'll never guess what happened yesterday! I was getting off the bus when I tripped and fell onto the pavement. I've cut my leg quite badly.
B (Show empathy.) _____
A Yes, it really hurt. I blame my friend Irene.
B (Ask for clarification.) _____
A Well, she persuaded me to wear these shoes. I'm not used to such high heels. She said I need to look smarter for my job. She says that customers expect receptionists to wear high heels.
B (Disagree politely.) _____
A Anyway, I've made one decision.
B (Guess what A will say.) _____
A That's right! Only comfortable shoes for me from now on!

23

4 REVIEW and PRACTICE

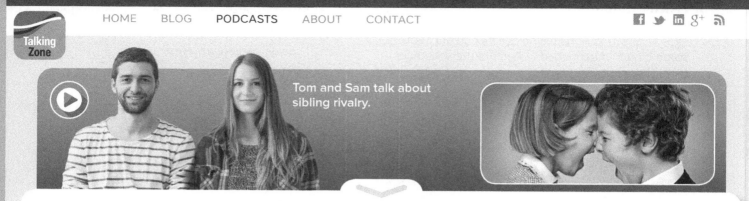

HOME   BLOG   **PODCASTS**   ABOUT   CONTACT

Tom and Sam talk about sibling rivalry.

LISTENING

1 ▶ 4.5 Listen to the podcast. What do you think the term 'sibling rivalry' means?
  a when parents do not treat their children equally
  b when one child is more successful than the others
  c when brothers and sisters argue and fight

2 ▶ 4.5 Listen again. Tick (✓) the words that you hear.
  1 silly _____
  2 stupid _____
  3 unreasonable _____
  4 bossy _____
  5 arrogant _____
  6 mean _____
  7 creative _____
  8 critical _____

3 ▶ 4.5 Listen again. Choose the best options.
  1 Now they're adults, Tom and his brothers
     a always behave like grown-ups.
     b get on well together.
     c still argue a lot.
  2 Carrie Fletcher has written a book about brothers and sisters who
     a don't change their personalities when they become adults.
     b had a bad relationship with their parents.
     c still argue although they're not children any more.
  3 According to her, if our siblings behaved badly as children, we
     a don't always realize that they're not the same now.
     b often continue to dislike them forever.
     c don't believe they're able to change.
  4 The proportion of people who thought their parents treated all the children equally was
     a 15%.   b 50%.   c 85%.
  5 She says that it's important
     a to be as successful as your siblings.
     b not to criticize your siblings.
     c not to blame your siblings for the way your parents behaved.
  6 According to Carrie Fletcher, it's possible to stop rivalry with your siblings by
     a agreeing to be polite and kind to each other.
     b making an effort to be nice to them.
     c accepting that they've changed.

READING

1 Read Tom's blog on page 25. Choose the best summary of what he says.
  a Tom went to a psychologist to learn how to be more positive and in this blog he shares what he has learned.
  b Tom has to fight against negative thoughts and he writes about some of the effective ways he has found of doing this.
  c Tom writes about different methods that people use to make themselves more positive because in his job it is important to sound happy.

2 Does Tom say these things in his blog? (Circle) Y (Yes) or N (No).
  1 His natural personality is not positive.   Y / N
  2 It took him many years to stop having negative thoughts.   Y / N
  3 It is possible to learn how to have positive thoughts.   Y / N
  4 Bad events are often not as important as we think they are.   Y / N
  5 His cousin is a difficult person to have as a visitor.   Y / N
  6 If you have negative thoughts about an experience, it will be better than you expected.   Y / N
  7 He finds it helpful to write down positive events.   Y / N
  8 You should stay away from people who make you miserable.   Y / N
  9 When he is at work, Sam helps to keep him happy.   Y / N
  10 You should only smile when you're feeling happy.   Y / N

REVIEW and PRACTICE 4

HOME   BLOG   PODCASTS   ABOUT   CONTACT

Tom writes about the power of the mind.

Think yourself positive!

In my job, it's essential to sound confident and cheerful, and I'm sure that most of our listeners think that this is my natural personality. Well, I'm sorry to disappoint you, but in fact I've had to work quite hard over the years to learn how to deal with the negative thoughts that sometimes come into my head – thoughts that could have destroyed my career if I'd allowed them to.

The good news, though, is that if I can make myself more positive, anyone can. You just need to learn the right techniques and, in my opinion anyway, you really should. After all, many scientific studies have proved that positive thinking has physical as well as mental benefits, and that has to be a good thing, right?

Obviously, I'm not a psychologist, but I've been thinking about the things that have worked best for me and I would say that number one is to try to keep your mind in the present. It's easy to be upset by something that has happened recently and to think about it again and again, like a bad movie playing in your head. But will it really matter in five years' time? Five months? Five weeks? Even five hours?

On the other hand, one of my personal bad habits was wasting energy on negative thoughts about the *future*. For example, if my cousin was coming to visit me, I'd drive myself crazy worrying that she'd be bored or that she'd want to go to expensive restaurants that I couldn't afford. So, by the time she actually arrived, I'd be annoyed with her for no reason at all! And that's the thing, isn't it? If you expect an experience to be bad, it probably will be!

Also, I keep a notebook by my bed. If I've been noticing my mood getting low, I make myself record all the good things that have happened that day. It sounds a bit silly, but it works for me. I also try to surround myself with positive friends, and of course my colleague Sam is like a ray of sunshine every day! I always seem to be in a good mood when she's around.

And, finally, however you're feeling, don't forget to smile! Practise in front of the mirror if you need to – it really does make a difference!

UNIT 5 Our planet

5A LANGUAGE

GRAMMAR: *so* and *such*; *so much/many, so little/few*

1 Complete the sentences with the words in the box.

   so few   such (x2)   so much
   such a   so   so many   so little

   1 I didn't realize the holiday cost _____ money.
   2 Mr Ashton is _____ good teacher!
   3 I didn't realize that studying could be _____ enjoyable.
   4 The beach is never crowded because _____ people know about it.
   5 This café makes _____ good hot chocolate!
   6 He made _____ effort to study, it's not surprising he failed the exam.
   7 We had _____ problems, I thought we would never finish the work.
   8 I don't think I've ever eaten _____ delicious doughnuts.

2 Are these sentences correct or incorrect? Cross out any mistakes and write the correct words at the end of the sentences.

   1 Travelling by plane is such bad for the environment. _____
   2 We had such brilliant teachers at that school. _____
   3 I was lonely because I had so few friends there. _____
   4 My sister has so lovely hair. _____
   5 I had so lovely time in Mexico. _____
   6 How can I write a good essay when I have so few time to do it? _____
   7 There was so much salt in the soup, I couldn't eat it. _____
   8 There are so much things to do in Paris. _____

VOCABULARY: The environment

3 Choose the correct options to complete the sentences.

   1 We all helped to pick up _____ from the park.
     a wildfires   b wildlife   c litter
   2 Aircraft produce a lot of _____.
     a carbon dioxide   b drought   c endangered species
   3 Because of the _____, the farmers had no water for their crops.
     a carbon dioxide   b wildfires   c drought
   4 We need to help protect the world's _____.
     a heat wave   b endangered species   c litter
   5 Hot, dry weather meant that the _____ spread quickly.
     a heat wave   b wildfires   c endangered species
   6 We went to the mountains to escape the _____.
     a litter   b drought   c heat wave
   7 We went to Africa to see the _____.
     a wildlife   b carbon dioxide   c wildfires

4 Complete the phrases with words that mean the same as the words in brackets.

   1 I'm really worried about c _ _ _ _ _ _ c _ _ _ _ _ (the way the weather is changing).
   2 We should rely much less on f _ _ _ _ _ f _ _ _ _ (energy sources such as coal and gas).
   3 We should use fuel that is e _ _ _ _ _ _ _ _ _ _ _ _ _ - f _ _ _ _ _ _ (not harmful to the planet).
   4 We could produce a lot more s _ _ _ _ e _ _ _ _ _ (electricity from the sun).
   5 We need to reduce our e _ _ _ _ _ c _ _ _ _ _ _ _ _ _ _ (the amount of fuel we use).
   6 We should buy household appliances that are e _ _ _ _ _ - e _ _ _ _ _ _ _ _ (only use small amounts of fuel).
   7 Solar power does not produce any t _ _ _ _ w _ _ _ _ (poisonous substances after it has been used).

PRONUNCIATION: Sentence stress with *so* and *such*

5 ▶5.1 In each sentence one of the stressed syllables is in **bold**. Read the sentences and underline the other stressed syllable. Listen and check.

   1 She's such a good **teach**er.
   2 I had such a terrible **head**ache.
   3 They cooked so much **food**.
   4 It was such a windy **day**.
   5 There are so many **peo**ple here.

26

SKILLS 5B

LISTENING: Identifying cause and effect

1 ▶ 5.2 Listen to James interviewing his guest, Grace, on the radio. Are the following statements true (T) or false (F)?

1 James says that everyone knows that cold weather makes them feel miserable. _____
2 Grace talks about how the weather affects our moods. _____
3 Grace gives two examples of how warm, sunny weather makes us treat other people better. _____
4 According to Grace, cold weather makes us notice the things that are around us more. _____
5 According to Grace, warm weather only affects us in a good way. _____
6 James suggests a different explanation for the way that warm weather causes people to become aggressive. _____
7 Grace says that weather influences people's behaviour even when they are outdoors for very short periods. _____
8 James jokes that people get annoyed on sunny days when they have to stay indoors. _____

2 ▶ 5.2 Listen again. Tick (✓) the sentences that you hear in the interview. Pay particular attention to the underlined words.

1 We all know that the weather <u>affects</u> our mood. _____
2 So how can the heat and the cold <u>impact</u> our behaviour? _____
3 But sunny weather has other – more surprising – <u>consequences</u>. _____
4 Did you know it <u>makes</u> us notice more about our surroundings? _____
5 Could this just be an <u>effect</u> of the better light? _____
6 Warm weather can <u>lead to</u> aggressive – even violent – behaviour. _____

3 ▶ 5.3 Listen to these phrases from the interview. Use the mark ‿ to show where a consonant sound ending one word is moved to the next word.

1 the weather affects our mood
2 she's going to talk about
3 let's start with a nice example
4 sunny weather has other effects
5 it makes us notice more
6 being stuck indoors on a lovely day

4 Choose the correct options to complete the sentences.

1 We had to walk twenty miles in the heat with heavy bags on our backs. It was completely *distressing / exhausting*.
2 We need a young, *lethargic / dynamic* leader who can change the whole organization.
3 I feel quite *pessimistic / optimistic* about the future of this company. I just know it's going to be a great success.
4 She's very *eager / passionate* about the environment and speaks with great energy on the subject.
5 I think this plant-based diet is really good for me. I feel so much more *grumpy / energetic* on it.
6 Poor Helen's having a few problems at home. She seemed a bit *motivated / down* when I saw her.
7 I haven't got the energy to do anything in this heat. I feel so *lethargic / enthusiastic*.
8 Carlo was in a terrible mood this morning. He was so *positive / grumpy*.

27

5C LANGUAGE

GRAMMAR: Future predictions

1 Choose the correct options to complete the sentences.

1 I can't come to the party with you now because I still have work to do, but I ____ later.
   a might come   b will have come
   c may have come

2 I'm sure we ____ glasses in 50 years' time.
   a may not be wearing   b aren't going to wear
   c won't be wearing

3 Look at all those dark clouds. I'm sure it ____.
   a might rain   b will be raining
   c 's going to rain

4 Ask Dad to drive you to the airport. I don't think he ____.
   a is going to mind   b 'll mind
   c might mind

5 She's certain that scientists ____ a way to stop climate change by then.
   a will have invented   b are going to invent
   c will be inventing

6 Do you think that Pablo ____ disappointed with his exam results?
   a will be being   b will
   c will be

7 Victoria says she definitely ____ any more because of the damage aircraft do to the environment.
   a might not fly   b isn't going to fly
   c won't have flown

2 Use the prompts to complete the sentences using *will* or *won't* with the future perfect or future continuous.

1 I hope that _____ by next week.
   (the builders / will / put / the roof on)

2 I plan to go travelling next summer.
   _____ by then.
   (I / will / finish / university)

3 Do you think we _____ in 2060?
   (will / still / use / gas and coal)

4 It is likely that _____ by a metre by 2100.
   (sea levels / will / rise)

5 Engineers are building a road across the desert but _____ by next year.
   (they / won't / finish / it)

6 We have planted a large forest. I hope that _____ hundreds of years from now.
   (people / will / enjoy / the trees)

7 Perhaps in twenty years, _____ a better way to generate electricity.
   (someone / will / invent)

VOCABULARY: Adjective prefixes

3 Match the two parts of the sentences.

1 I think it was rather dis ____
2 We had to learn a list of ir ____
3 We were disappointed by her im ____
4 I didn't know it was il ____
5 He gets annoyed when people mis ____
6 Accidents are un ____
7 It's fine to use these phrases in in ____
8 It was extremely im ____

a legal to take shells from the beach.
b pronounce his name.
c avoidable without the correct safety equipment.
d honest to pretend you didn't see her email.
e polite to ignore her.
f mature behaviour.
g formal situations.
h regular verbs.

4 Complete the words in the text with the prefixes *dis-, im-, in-, un-, il-, ir-,* or *mis-*.

This morning I received an ¹____expected piece of good news: my boss has decided to retire. He's a lovely man, but he's so ²____organized. His office is really messy, and he gets incredibly ³____patient when he can't find the things he needs, and then wastes my time chatting about totally ⁴____relevant things such as football. He goes to meetings and comes back with lots of ⁵____spelled and almost ⁶____legible notes that I can't read. I also have to check his sales figures, which are usually ⁷____accurate, as well as dealing with ⁸____satisfied customers, who often accuse him of giving them ⁹____leading information about our products. It's a mystery why he's stayed in the job so long when he's obviously so ¹⁰____suitable for it.

PRONUNCIATION: *will have*

5 ▶5.4 Read the sentences aloud. Remember to pronounce *have* as /əv/. Listen and check.

1 Will we have covered all the topics by June?
2 We'll have found a cure for many more diseases.
3 I won't have finished my degree by then.
4 In fifteen years, the children will have grown up.
5 Won't they have completed the new road by May?
6 I don't think you'll have finished by 3:00 p.m.

SKILLS 5D

WRITING: Writing an opinion essay

Should people take more PERSONAL RESPONSIBILITY for the environment?

A Another reason is that some of our actions are more harmful than we probably realize. A flight from Amsterdam to Beijing will put around 740 kg of CO_2 into the atmosphere: recycling everything for a year will not save that amount or anything close to it. [1]_____, over 25 million people travel through New York's JFK airport alone each year. If every one of those people took one less flight a year, it would make a big difference.

B [2]_____, we should not wait for governments to take action on climate change. We all have a responsibility towards the planet we live on. We should do our best to take care of it and therefore make it more likely that other people, including politicians, will take care of it, too.

C It is easy to feel hopeless when we think about the huge problem of climate change. Many people think that only governments can make the significant changes we need to prevent it. [3]_____, they don't understand why they should take personal responsibility, especially if it makes their own lives harder. Why should they cycle to work if everyone else comes by car? However, this attitude is wrong: we all need to play our part in helping to save the planet.

D One reason is that the more we make changes in our own lives, the more we are likely to influence other people. If your colleagues see you on your bike, they might consider cycling, too. [4]_____, the politicians who represent us can be influenced by knowing what is important to us, and they are more likely to listen to us if we do things which show that we want to protect the environment [5]_____ just talking about it.

---

1 Read the opinion essay and number paragraphs A–D in the correct order 1–4.

1 ___
2 ___
3 ___
4 ___

2 Complete gaps 1–5 with formal linkers a–e.

a Nevertheless
b as opposed to
c Consequently
d In sum
e Similarly

3 Imagine you are answering the same essay question but have the opposite view. Write the following:

1 a thesis statement:_____
2 a topic sentence for a paragraph arguing that individual people cannot make a difference:_____
3 a topic sentence for a paragraph arguing that governments control what industries do:_____
4 the first sentence of a concluding paragraph: _____

4 Write an opinion essay on the following topic:

Should we be prepared to accept a lower standard of living in order to protect the environment?

- Provide a clear thesis statement.
- Start each paragraph with a topic statement.
- Support your thesis statement with examples, facts, figures etc.
- Summarize the key points in the concluding paragraph.
- Use at least three formal linkers to connect your ideas.

5 REVIEW and PRACTICE

Talking Zone

HOME   BLOG   **PODCASTS**   ABOUT   CONTACT

Tom and Sam talk about protecting the environment.

LISTENING

1 ▶ 5.5 Listen to the podcast and choose the best summary of Tom's plan for this week.

a He's going to try to find the best app to help him to protect the environment.
b He's going to use some apps that will help him to protect the environment.
c He's going to make his home more energy-efficient.

2 ▶ 5.5 Listen again. Are the sentences true (T), false (F) or doesn't say (DS)?

1 Earth Day started thirty years ago. ___
2 Earth Day started as a result of an accident that happened. ___
3 Tom will be using three apps. ___
4 He will use one of the apps when he's buying food. ___
5 Tom thinks he will do less driving as a result of using one of the apps. ___
6 Tom usually drives a lot. ___
7 Another app will tell Tom how much energy he is using in his home. ___
8 The makers of the litter app want to help solve the problem of littering. ___

READING

1 Read Ellie's blog on page 31 and number topics a–f in the order that they appear (1–6).

a a new way of cleaning the seas ___
b the effect of bad news on the author's mood ___
c the increase in global temperatures ___
d the areas of land that are being protected ___
e the people who are trying to help the environment ___
f animals that may soon not exist ___

2 Choose the best options to complete the sentences.

1 Ellie says that depressing predictions about the environment
   a sometimes make her feel pessimistic.
   b are not true.
   c always make her feel pessimistic.
2 According to Ellie
   a there is no good news about the environment.
   b the news about the environment is mainly good.
   c there is good *and* bad news about the environment.
3 Ellie claims that things are being done to protect the environment but we
   a never hear about them.
   b sometimes don't hear about them.
   c are not interested in them.
4 In Chile and Papua New Guinea
   a most of the trees are being cut down.
   b no trees are being cut down.
   c some of the trees are now protected.
5 The situation in relation to Uganda's mountain gorillas is
   a extremely hopeful.
   b slightly hopeful.
   c not at all hopeful.
6 To help solve the problem of plastic, some supermarkets
   a are using less plastic in their packaging.
   b have stopped selling some items.
   c are only using paper in their packaging.

REVIEW and PRACTICE 5

HOME   BLOG   PODCASTS   ABOUT   CONTACT

Guest blogger Ellie gives some reasons for us to be cheerful about the environment.

Green – and happy!

Scientists say that by the end of the century, increased levels of carbon dioxide in the atmosphere will have caused the average global temperature to rise by two degrees. As a result, heatwaves, droughts and wildfires will all be happening much more frequently. With so many pessimistic and distressing predictions about the future of the planet, it's not always easy to be positive. Now, I'm cheerful by nature, but even I sometimes struggle to feel optimistic about the future. But being miserable isn't going to help. And there's some good news out there, I promise you. With this blog – the first of many – I aim to tell you about it!

First up, there are some passionate and dynamic people out there, making a real difference. (It has to be said, it helps when they have money!) Did you know, for example, that the Leonardo DiCaprio Foundation has donated huge sums of money to organizations that protect endangered species and the environment? Or that other charitable foundations are protecting our oceans by preventing illegal fishing and plastic pollution? We don't always hear about the good stuff that's happening.

We're always hearing about the world's disappearing forests and that is, of course, *extremely bad* news for our planet. But in several parts of the world, for example in Chile and Papua New Guinea, *new* conservation areas are actually being created and existing conservation areas are being expanded. In these places, the cutting down of trees will be forbidden and wildlife in all its many forms will find a home for generations to come. This is all very encouraging.

Meanwhile, in Uganda's Bwindi National Park, there's such good news about the mountain gorilla. Their numbers have actually gone up! Admittedly, they're still 'critically endangered' but at least there's now hope that these beautiful and amazing creatures will have a future.

We're all *finally* waking up to the fact that plastic is not fantastic. Governments the world over have started banning the sale of certain plastic products. Supermarkets are reducing

the amount of plastic in their packaging, replacing it with paper or other substances that will decay naturally. Major cities in the world will soon get drinking fountains, reducing the need for people to buy mineral water in plastic bottles. Things can change and *are* changing.

In the meantime, new technologies are being developed all the while that can be used for environmental purposes. There are astonishing machines that can suck rubbish out of the oceans, knives and forks that you can actually eat (rather than throw away) and apps that can help with anything from car-sharing to choosing local food when it's in season.

There is hope, and don't you forget it!

31

UNIT 6 Habits and change

6A LANGUAGE

GRAMMAR: The habitual past

1 Complete the sentences with *used*, *use*, *would* or *was*.

1 Our parents never _____ to let us play near the river.
2 Our grandmother _____ usually be at the station to meet us.
3 Did you _____ to play with dolls when you were little?
4 We didn't _____ to have a TV in our house.
5 I found Irene boring because she _____ always talking about her horses.
6 After dinner, we _____ sit and chat for a while.
7 We had a car but it _____ always breaking down.
8 We all _____ to help on the farm.

2 Find six mistakes in the conversation. Cross out the mistakes and write the correct version above them.

A When you were a child, did your parents both used to work?
B Yes. I used to grow up on a farm, so in fact, everybody was expected to work. Before school, my sister would feed the chickens and I would collect the eggs. I would hate getting up so early! Mum and Dad both worked on the farm during the day, but Mum was always waiting for us when we got home. She never use to leave us alone when we were young.
A Would you like living on a farm?
B Yes, I loved it!
A My uncle was a farmer, too. I used to stay at his farm a few times in the school holidays and I loved everything about it except the farm dog, because he was always barking at me!

VOCABULARY: Expressions with *time*

3 Choose the correct prepositions to complete the sentences.

1 The concert is at 8, but I don't expect it will start *in / on / at* time.
2 I've been learning French *for / from / at* some time now.
3 Do you think we'll be there *in / for / on* time to see Maria before she leaves?
4 I used to go to a lot of baseball matches because we were living in the USA *in / from / at* the time.
5 I like my job, but it gets a bit stressful *for / from / at* time to time.
6 Make sure you add the eggs one *in / at / on* a time.
7 If everyone helps, we'll get this work done *on / from / in* no time.

4 Complete the phrases with the missing words.

1 There's no hurry to finish eating, so please _____ your time.
2 While we were waiting, we played cards to _____ the time.
3 I think you work too hard. You need to _____ time to have some fun!
4 Are you ready? Our guests will be arriving _____ time now.
5 I run the same route every week, and I time _____ to see if I'm improving.
6 This road is so dangerous – it's only a _____ of time before there's an accident.
7 Why don't you keep your keys in a safe place? We _____ so much time searching for them!

PRONUNCIATION: /s/ and /z/ in *use(d)*

5 ▶ 6.1 Read the sentences aloud, being careful to pronounce *use(d)* correctly. Listen and check.

1 My great-grandparents didn't use to have electricity in their house.
2 I used to use my exercise bike every day, but I don't now.
3 Didn't Samuel use to play the drums?
4 Diego didn't want me to use his laptop, but I used it anyway.
5 Have you ever used a personal trainer?
6 We used to live in Panama City.

32

SKILLS 6B

READING: Understanding non-literal meaning

Can a leopard change its spots?

We all describe each other in terms of character traits. We are 'cheerful' or 'miserable', 'hard-working' or 'lazy', etc. Yet personality has been a controversial subject over the years. Some psychologists have even argued that, contrary to popular belief, there is no such thing as a personality trait. Our behaviour, they claimed, was just the result of the situations that we found ourselves in.

Generally, however, research has seemed to suggest that the opposite is true and that character traits do indeed exist. In studies, when people are observed in a variety of situations, they tend to show more or less the same type of behaviour in all of those situations. This shouldn't be a great surprise to anyone. After all, when we describe a friend as 'polite', we are thinking of the way he or she speaks to other people in class, at the train station or in a restaurant and not just in one of these places.

What is less clear, however, is whether those personality traits are fixed or, on the contrary, change over time. It used to be thought that our traits developed throughout childhood and early adulthood but were then set in stone for life. A recently published study suggests that this may not be the case. A group of people were observed over several decades and their behaviour studied. Their characteristics after forty or more years were very different from the traits that they had shown in their youth. After all, everyone knows a person whose character has changed significantly over the years. My husband's father, for example, a strict and controlling parent in his thirties and forties, later became the kindest, sweetest grandfather the world has ever known, as gentle as a lamb.

The truth of the matter seems to be that personality traits are generally fairly fixed, but they can change gradually over the course of a lifetime. Certain experiences tend to cause personality change more than others. Great career success and tragedy are two of these. However, what's encouraging is that the changes are usually positive, most people becoming nicer and calmer as they grow older.

1 Tick (✓) the statements that are true.
  1 Some experts have claimed that personality does not exist. _____
  2 Most people agree that our characters are made up of particular qualities. _____
  3 People usually show different characteristics in different situations. _____
  4 Previously, it was believed that our personalities were formed in early childhood. _____
  5 In the past, psychologists thought that our personalities stayed the same for all our adult lives. _____
  6 Most people know someone whose personality is different to how it was when he/she was younger. _____
  7 When people's characters change, this generally happens quite quickly. _____
  8 When very sad things happen to people, it can change the way that they behave. _____

2 Identify whether each underlined phrase is an exaggeration (E), a comparison (C), a personification (P) or an idiom (I). There are two of each.
  1 … our traits developed throughout childhood and early adulthood but were then set in stone for life. _____
  2 My husband's father […] later became the kindest, sweetest grandfather the world has ever known … _____
  3 … became the kindest, sweetest grandfather the world has ever known, as gentle as a lamb. _____
  4 As regards Helen's remark, I've never heard anything so stupid in all my life! _____
  5 There's a slice of chocolate cake in the kitchen and it's calling my name! _____
  6 It broke her heart when Jamie left. _____
  7 Once outside, we were viciously attacked by the rain and the wind. _____
  8 Oh, you poor thing! Your hands are as cold as ice! _____

3 Complete each phrase with one word.
  1 _____ to popular belief, we do not need animal products in our diet in order to be healthy.
  2 Most people worry that their kitchens aren't clean enough. In fact, the _____ is true and they're probably too clean!
  3 The truth of the _____ is that most of us spend far too much time sitting down.
  4 She certainly wasn't lazy. On the _____, she rarely had a break from work.

33

6C LANGUAGE

GRAMMAR: *be used to* and *get used to*

1 Choose the correct options to complete the sentences.

1. I've been getting up at 5 a.m. for two years now, so I _____ to it.
   a get used   b 'm used   c used
2. This is my new bike. I haven't _____ to it yet.
   a been used   b used   c got used
3. _____ to a new school or college can be hard.
   a Getting used   b Being used   c Using
4. It took Rafaela a long time to _____ to the fact that Daniel had gone.
   a get used   b be used   c used
5. I could tell that Lucia _____ to such hard work.
   a didn't use   b didn't get used   c wasn't used

2 Complete the sentences with the correct form of (*not*) *be used to* or (*not*) *get used to* and the verbs in brackets.

1. I _____ (cook) for so many people.
2. Manuel had worked in a café for years, so he _____ (talk) to lots of different people.
3. Is it hard to _____ (live) on a boat?
4. In the UK I had to _____ (drive) on the left.
5. These boots can be uncomfortable, especially if you _____ (wear) them.

VOCABULARY: Expressions with prepositions

3 Complete the text with the expressions in the box.

> advantage of   fed up with   approve of   cared about
> advised me against   confused about   possibility of
> comfortable with   anxious about   sympathetic to

As a teenager, I was very ¹_____ what I wanted to do for my career. All I really ²_____ was acting, but my parents ³_____ it because acting is such a risky career.
After I finished my degree, I got a job with a bank. I soon got ⁴_____ it: the work was boring. My flatmate was ⁵_____ my situation and asked me if I'd ever considered the ⁶_____ becoming a teacher. At first I was ⁷_____ dealing with the kids, but I found that I loved teaching, and felt very ⁸_____ them. The other ⁹_____ working in a school is that I now spend a lot of time helping out with the drama club, which I love. Luckily, my parents ¹⁰_____ my new career, too!

4 Complete the crossword.

Across

6. She watches TV every evening – she's absolutely _____ with soap operas! (8)
7. What was his _____ to Martin calling him an idiot? (8)
8. The _____ of living in Scotland is that the weather is terrible. (12)
9. He's _____ to a cheaper ticket because he's under 16. (8)
10. My grandmother is very independent – she _____ on doing all her own housework and gardening. (7)

Down

1. I must remember to _____ Diego on his fantastic exam results. (12)
2. I'm _____ to chocolate – I eat it every day. (8)
3. Their story about seeing ghosts was silly – I don't _____ in them at all. (7)
4. You should be very _____ of strange emails – don't click on any links in them! (10)
5. She was extremely upset when they _____ her of lying. (7)

PRONUNCIATION: *be used to* and *get used to*

5 ▶6.2 Read the sentences aloud. Pay attention to the /ə/ sound in *to*. Listen and check.

1. I'll never get used to getting up so early!
2. We're not used to this hot weather.
3. These children aren't used to sitting still for so long.
4. You'll get used to the noise of the traffic.
5. She's used to telling other people what to do.
6. We're slowly getting used to working together.

SKILLS 6D

SPEAKING: Challenging assumptions

1 ▶ 6.3 Listen to Luis and Eva discussing their plans for a cheap holiday. Tick (✓) the phrases you hear that are connected with solving problems.

1 If you ask me, … ____
2 We could either … or … ____
3 We could always … ____
4 Why not …? ____
5 We could … instead of … ____
6 Like what? ____
7 You mean …? ____
8 The point I'm making is … ____
9 I'm just saying … ____
10 Is it worth it, though? ____
11 But is that really a good idea? ____
12 What difference would it make? ____

2 ▶ 6.3 Listen again and complete the sentences that Luis and Eva use to challenge each other's assumptions.

1 Just because we're _____ doesn't mean we can't _____.
2 True, but it's still _____, isn't it?
3 We can _____ in the daytime regardless of _____ at night.
4 _____ is one thing, cycling all the way to the coast carrying a tent is _____.
5 _____ has nothing to do with _____ ourselves.

3 Use your own ideas to write responses that challenge A's assumptions. Use phrases from exercise 2.

1 A I go jogging most days, so I think I'll be fine to run a marathon.
   B _____ is one thing, but _____ is quite another.
2 A You can't walk to work if it's raining.
   B _____
3 A I know he loves me because he gives me lots of expensive presents.
   B _____
4 A It's better to send a birthday card late than not to send one at all.
   B _____
5 A Let's stay in our hotel room. We only have two hours before we need to be at the station.
   B _____

4 ▶ 6.4 Complete the conversation. Then listen and check.

A If you ¹_____ me, there's no point going to Sara's party. She's invited so many people that we won't get a chance to talk to her.
B True, but I think it will ²_____ be fun. Just ³_____ she'll be busy with her other guests ⁴_____ we can't enjoy the party.
A Is it ⁵_____ it, though? It's a long way to go, isn't it, and taxis are so expensive.
B We could ⁶_____ get a bus ⁷_____ maybe see if someone will give us a lift. Sara's parties are always great, and she's hired a DJ for this one.
A But ⁸_____ if we can't?
B I don't know. The ⁹_____ I'm making is that I think we'll have a good time no ¹⁰_____ whether Sara has time to talk to us or not, so I really think we should go.
A OK, you've convinced me! We could ¹¹_____ share a taxi with someone else if we can't get a lift.

5 Imagine your friend needs to pass an English exam but has a bad teacher. Write a short conversation between you and your friend. Include phrases for making suggestions and offering or asking for clarification.

35

6 REVIEW and PRACTICE

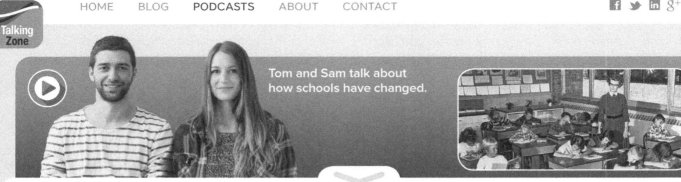

LISTENING

1 ▶ 6.5 Listen to Tom and Sam's interview with Tony and tick (✓) the correct sentences.

1 School life is different now from how it was when Tony was at school. ____
2 Teachers were less easy-going when he was at school. ____
3 Teachers used the same punishments when Tony was at school as they do today. ____
4 Tony's teachers made sure that he made good progress. ____
5 Tony thinks today's pupils have too much stress. ____
6 He is pleased that pupils stay at school longer now. ____

2 ▶ 6.5 Listen again and complete the sentences with one or two words.

1 When Tony was at school, pupils had to _____ when the teacher came in.
2 Pupils who talked in class had to _____.
3 Nobody wanted to be seen outside the classroom by the _____.
4 Tony used to _____ by staring out of the window.
5 Tony thinks that schools are obsessed with _____.
6 He thinks that pupils nowadays need time to _____ and be kids.
7 Tony was only 15 when he _____.
8 His first job was in a _____.
9 Nowadays, pupils have to stay in _____ education until they are 18.
10 Tony believes that a _____ means a better life.

READING

1 Read Sam's blog on page 37. Put these strange family habits a–f in the order that Sam mentions them (1–6).

a doing strange things to bring luck ____
b continuing to pronounce words like a child ____
c keeping things in strange places ____
d eating unusual food ____
e pretending a pet is a real person ____
f using a toy in a strange way ____

2 Are the sentences true (T), false (F) or doesn't say (DS)?

1 Silvana likes to have milk with her ice-cream. ____
2 Silvana makes sugar sandwiches for her family. ____
3 Sam's family buy her presents and say they are from her cat. ____
4 Sam thinks it is funny that Tom's family puts a doll in the fruit bowl. ____
5 The tradition of taking a potato to exams has existed in Dan's family for a long time. ____
6 Lola's family think that folded crisps are unlucky. ____
7 Sam and her sister have a strange habit connected with going up and down their parents' stairs. ____
8 Sam's cousin expected the waiter to know the word 'marbies'. ____

REVIEW and PRACTICE **6**

HOME **BLOG** PODCASTS ABOUT CONTACT

Sam writes about the strange habits some families have.

It runs in the family!

Have you ever said or done something that your friends think is really weird? It happened to me yesterday when I was at my friend Silvana's house. She offered me some ice-cream and, without thinking, I asked for some milk to pour on it. It was only when I noticed the expression on her face that I realized something was wrong. Doesn't everyone put milk on their ice-cream? Apparently not!

It can be embarrassing when you realize that some of the things that you're used to doing when you're with your own family aren't shared by most other people. Once Silvana stopped laughing, she admitted that she herself has been addicted to sugar sandwiches ever since her grandmother gave them to her as a child. And that her boyfriend puts mayonnaise on bananas. Now that's weird!

The thing is, all our families do things that we think are normal until we meet other people who tell us that they're not. I'm in my twenties now, and I still get birthday presents 'from the cat'. Tom thinks that's strange, but his family keep their bread in the microwave oven, and they have a doll they call the 'No Fruit Dolly' which they put in the fruit bowl when it's empty!

Some habits go back for generations. My friend Dan's grandfather discovered a potato in his jacket pocket after he'd passed his driving test. After that, his dad would always take a potato with him if he had an exam of any kind, and now Dan and his sisters do the same! It seems that lots of families have strange activities they perform to bring them luck. In my friend Lola's family, if they find a crisp that's completely folded over, they can make a wish, but only if they press the crisp against their forehead and break it first! Mind you, I shouldn't criticize them for that because even today, neither my sister nor I will tread on the third stair of my parents' staircase in case it brings us bad luck!

And then there are family words that make no sense at all to other people. Often, they're childish mispronunciations that never got replaced with their adult versions. My 30-year-old cousin still insists on calling curtains 'turtens' and biscuits 'usk-usks'. I'm used to it now, but I was with her in a restaurant recently when she accidentally asked the waiter for extra 'marbies' on her pizza – her childhood word for 'tomatoes'. Her face went bright red when she realized her mistake!

Anyway, I'll stop now because I'm hungry and my sister is making chocolate omelettes for lunch ... oh, wait, are you telling me that it's only my family that eats them?

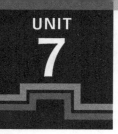

UNIT 7 Lifelong learning

7A LANGUAGE

GRAMMAR: Relative clauses; reduced and comment clauses

1 Choose the correct options to complete the sentences.

1 Is it the play *where / who / which* we saw in London?
2 In the movie, Lopez plays the guy *that / whose / who* brother is a gangster.
3 Luis, *which / who / whose* I work with, has seen Adele in concert five times.
4 My parents paid for my holiday, *that / what / which* was really generous of them.
5 Anyone *requires / required / requiring* more information should speak to Julia.
6 Applications *submitted / submitting / submit* after this date will not be considered.

2 Use the prompts to write sentences with the present simple that contain relative clauses. Sentences 1–3 should contain reduced clauses and sentences 4–6 should contain comment clauses.

1 the blond guy / sit / next to / Daniel / be / my boss
   _____
2 he / usually / throw away / any food / leave / at the end of the day
   _____
3 the woman / eat an ice cream / be / Sophie
   _____
4 My mother / often / call me / at work, / be irritating
   _____
5 Sara / play / her music / loud, / be really annoying
   _____
6 the train ticket / cost / £80, / I not afford
   _____

VOCABULARY: Collocations with *attend*, *get*, *make* and *submit*

3 Complete the sentences with the correct form of *attend*, *get*, *make* or *submit*.

1 I've _____ all my lectures this term!
2 He was asked to _____ a report on the economy.
3 It's extremely important that we _____ this message across to the public.
4 Which college does he _____?
5 She clearly hadn't prepared for the meeting and she _____ matters worse by being late!
6 She'd never _____ a job application before.

4 Complete the texts with the correct words.

Working from home has its good points and its not-so-good points, as anyone who makes a ¹l_____ as a freelancer will tell you. On the plus side, you get to choose the hours that you work. For example, if it's a gorgeous morning, you can make the ²m_____ of it by going out for a walk and starting work a bit later. Little things make a big ³d_____, too – like being able to play music and have your dog sit at your feet as you work. But, of course, there are disadvantages, too. You submit a ⁴p_____ to a publisher for a book that you'd like to write and it's very disappointing when it's rejected. Also, it's sometimes hard to get ⁵h_____ of colleagues that you need to speak to when they're working in an office. You also have to accept that working on your own can be quite lonely. I attend ⁶c_____ related to my profession twice a year, but apart from that, I don't spend time with other writers. To make ⁷m_____ worse, I live out in the country where there aren't so many people. Not everyone would enjoy that.

PRONUNCIATION: Comment clauses

5 ▶ 7.1 Read the sentences aloud. Pay attention to the pause after the comma and the falling intonation after it. Listen and check.

1 Petra bought me a T-shirt for my birthday, which was kind of her.
2 The train was half an hour late, which meant that I missed my plane.
3 Tom recommended somewhere to stay, which was really helpful.
4 Olga blames Julia for the accident, which I think is a bit unfair.
5 There was a shop just near to the apartment, which was very convenient.
6 The first course was a spicy fish dish, which she didn't like at all.

SKILLS 7B

LISTENING: Identifying sequence

1 ▶ 7.2 Listen to the interview and choose the correct options.

1 Mariana says that when she was at school
   a she enjoyed maths more than any other subject.
   b her least favourite subject was maths.
   c she was very good at maths.

2 At school, Gabriel
   a learned basic maths successfully.
   b was quite good at maths.
   c found it very hard to learn maths.

3 Gabriel says
   a his school teacher was good at explaining maths rules.
   b he couldn't understand what his school teacher said.
   c his school teacher was bad at explaining maths rules.

4 Why does Gabriel think he couldn't learn maths at school?
   a His teacher kept telling him he couldn't do it.
   b His sister kept telling him he couldn't do it.
   c He thought he couldn't do it.

5 What do we know about the teacher at Gabriel's evening class?
   a She loves maths.
   b She's a brilliant mathematician.
   c She explains things well.

6 What did Gabriel learn in his evening class?
   a It is better to work slowly, from one stage to the next.
   b You should discover the rules by yourself and not ask too many questions.
   c You have to be patient to learn maths.

2 ▶ 7.2 Listen again. Focus on the way Gabriel gives tips or advice. Complete the sentences.

1 Basically, _____ a very simple rule, _____ learn a more complex rule.

2 And – and this is so important – _____ you have a question, _____!

3 _____ you're totally confused _____ your teacher a question!

4 And, _____, *never* give up!

3 ▶ 7.3 Read the sentences aloud. Pay attention to the underlined schwa /ə/ sound. Listen and repeat.

1 You c<u>a</u>n come too if you like.
2 What shall we eat f<u>or</u> dinner?
3 She worked <u>as</u> a teacher.
4 Someday I'd like t<u>o</u> go there.
5 <u>At</u> the café, we had coffee <u>a</u>nd cake.
6 He w<u>as</u> standing next t<u>o</u> Jamie.

4 Complete the words.

1 Not everyone is c_____ of dealing with such stressful situations.

2 This is quite advanced physics. Even I s_____ to understand it and I'm a scientist.

3 He can't s_____ to understand quite basic instructions. I wonder why?

4 Sarah gives great talks – she has a real t_____ for it.

5 I think I was reasonably s_____ at explaining the rules. Most of the children seemed to understand.

6 I'm afraid I completely f_____ to learn Spanish when I was living in Spain.

7 She spoke so quickly. I f_____ it h_____ to follow her.

8 Unfortunately, I couldn't quite m_____ to finish my essay in time.

9 He was giving tips on how to s_____ at learning a musical instrument.

10 He's p_____ good at cooking.

7C LANGUAGE

GRAMMAR: Present and future real conditions

1 Complete the sentences with the words in the box. Use two words twice.

| soon | long | as | even | unless | provided |

1 _____ if not many people come, we can still have fun!
2 The event will take place outside _____ it's raining, in which case it will be indoors.
3 We'll finish the work before lunch as _____ as enough people turn up to help.
4 We'll leave the house as _____ as it stops snowing.
5 It's still enjoyable to sing in a choir _____ if you don't have the best voice!
6 She says she'll come to the concert _____ long as we pay for her.
7 _____ she starts speaking to the other children, she's not going to make any friends.
8 They'll start building their new house in June _____ they get permission.

2 Complete the sentences with the verbs in brackets.

1 Lucia _____ (look after) the children provided we _____ (pay) her.
2 You _____ (be) safe as long as you _____ (travel) in a group at all times.
3 Unless we _____ (do) something to stop it, these animals _____ (be) extinct in a few years.
4 We _____ (call) you as soon as the plane _____ (land).
5 I think you _____ (enjoy) yourself even if you _____ (go) on holiday on your own.
6 I _____ (not invite) Carlo to the party unless Jess _____ (insist).
7 Provided there _____ (be) no delays, we _____ (reach) Oxford by 2:00.
8 We _____ (have) lunch as soon as Sophia and Gloria _____ (get) here.

VOCABULARY: Mind and memory

3 Complete the sentences with the correct form of the verbs in the box. Use one verb twice.

| cross | change | make up | boost | keep |

1 When you pack for the trip, _____ in mind that it gets very cold at night in the mountains.
2 There are various ways to _____ your memory, such as getting enough sleep and exercise.
3 I can't _____ my mind whether to go to Sophia's party tonight.
4 If you _____ your mind about going to the cinema, text me and I'll buy a ticket for you, too.
5 I've never been to a vegetarian restaurant but I'll try to _____ an open mind. It might be fantastic!
6 I assumed Jack would come with us. It never even _____ my mind that he might not want to go.

4 Complete the text with the correct words.

My sister's amazing – if you tell her your birthday once, she'll remember it forever. I'm just the opposite – I have such a bad ¹m_____. Once, at school, a teacher asked us to learn a short poem by ²h_____ for homework. The next day, she asked me to say the poem out loud in front of the class. I stood up and my mind just went ³b_____ – I couldn't ⁴r_____ a single line! It was awful! There are other things, too. My mum is always having to ⁵r_____ me to do things or I'll just forget. And experiences, too – even special experiences that most people would find ⁶m_____. A few months after they happen, I've forgotten all about them.

PRONUNCIATION: Sentence stress

5 ⏵ 7.4 Listen to the sentences. Which are the two stressed words in each underlined phrase?

1 I usually take her a present even if it's only a few flowers.
2 You can use my bike as long as you bring it back.
3 Maria will go to university next September provided she passes all her exams.
4 Unless you give her some money, she won't be able to go to New York.
5 He can borrow my car as long as he drives it carefully.
6 Provided the weather is nice, you should have a nice trip!

SKILLS 7D

WRITING: Writing a set of guidelines

Preparing for an exam

1 You've been learning a subject for months, even years, and yet you're going to be judged on your performance on one single day. No wonder exams are so stressful! Here are some tips to make sure you get the mark you really deserve.

2 _____

Some people like to learn everything at the last minute, but that doesn't work for most of us. I'll never forget the French exam where I decided to revise the night before but had such a bad headache I couldn't. What a disaster! **Besides**, most exams test far more information than you can revise in one evening.

3 _____

Have you ever had an experience where you thought you understood something, but when you tried to explain it, you found you didn't really? Explaining what you're learning to your friends or family can really test your understanding. **In addition**, I find that saying it out loud helps me to remember.

4 _____

You won't do your best if you don't feel your best. Try to eat well (resist junk food if you can), and drink plenty of water. **Moreover**, it's important to take a break now and then – a tired brain isn't an efficient brain! I know I work much better after a quick walk in the fresh air.

5 Lastly, here's my most important piece of advice for you: do past papers, more past papers and then more past papers! If you do that, you'll really get to know the exam and what to expect. I didn't do that for my last maths exam because I was confident I could do everything, but the form of the questions wasn't what I was expecting, and I didn't get a very good mark. Good luck!

1 Read the blog post and choose the correct headings a–e for paragraphs 2–4. There are two extra headings.

  a Pretend to be the teacher
  b Be good to yourself
  c Work with a friend
  d Give yourself enough time
  e Give yourself a reward for hard work

2 <u>Underline</u> the sentences in paragraphs 2, 3, 4 and 5 that give the reason for each tip. Some paragraphs have more than one reason. Now use your own ideas to give a reason for each of the tips below.

  1 When you are choosing a college or university course, use your heart as well as your head – think about which subjects you really love.
  _____
  2 If your employer offers you the chance to go on a training course, take it!
  _____
  3 Look for relevant study apps that you can use on your phone.
  _____

3 Look at the linkers in **bold** in the blog post. Choose the correct options to complete the sentences.

  1 Degrees last at least three years. *Moreover / However*, in some countries they can be very expensive.
  2 It can be difficult to find time for study. *Besides / Nevertheless*, it's usually worth making the effort.
  3 It's easy to find books on most subjects. *In addition / Consequently*, you can go to an evening class.
  4 It's best to study something you enjoy. *Moreover / However*, you need maths for some jobs.
  5 The university closest to you isn't necessarily the best one. *Besides / Similarly*, going to live in another city can be a great experience.

4 Choose one of the topics below and write a blog post giving a set of guidelines.

  1 *Choosing a course, for instance at university*
  2 *Continuing to learn all your life*
  3 *Making time for study if you have a busy life*

  • Write a short introduction explaining the purpose of your post.
  • Include 3–4 important tips, organized into paragraphs.
  • Give reasons for each tip and include examples or personal experience.
  • Use linkers to add ideas.

41

7 REVIEW and PRACTICE

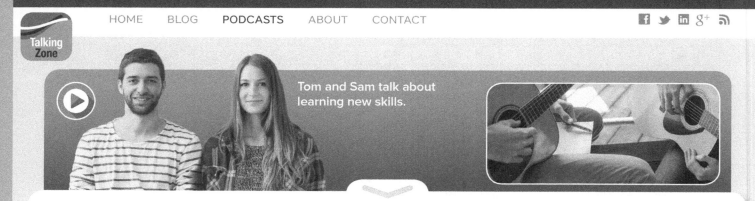

LISTENING

1 ▶ 7.5 Listen to the podcast and number a–e in the order that you hear them (1–5).

a Alice gives the reason for practising five (and not seven) days a week. ____
b Sam says the name of the guest's blog. ____
c Sam mentions a habit of Barack Obama's. ____
d Alice says that her learning hour is in the mornings. ____
e Tom admits he has stopped trying to learn the guitar. ____

2 ▶ 7.5 Listen again and choose the correct options to complete the sentences.

1 Tom is no longer playing the guitar because
 a he has lost interest.
 b he doesn't have time.
 c the lessons are too expensive.
2 Alice wrote a blog about
 a spending an hour a day learning.
 b making the best use of time.
 c playing musical instruments.
3 She recommends studying five days a week
 a so that you don't get tired and make yourself ill.
 b so that your weekends are free.
 c because on some days it isn't possible to study.
4 Barack Obama _____ for an hour every day.
 a played an instrument
 b read
 c studied
5 Alice says you should study or practise
 a in the morning.
 b in the evening.
 c at the same time each day.
6 Alice likes studying in the mornings when she
 a is on her own.
 b has lots of energy.
 c can think clearly.

READING

1 Read Hannah's blog on page 43 and choose the best summary.

a Hannah describes all the things that other schools do badly.
b Hannah writes about a typical day at her school.
c Hannah describes what she thinks is special about her school.

2 Are the sentences true (T), false (F) or doesn't say (DS)?

1 Hannah has already met Tom and Sam. ____
2 She thought they were both very funny. ____
3 Hannah believes that only happy, healthy students make progress. ____
4 She thinks that teachers generally disagree with this opinion. ____
5 Hannah says schools do nothing to improve the well-being of their students. ____
6 The English teachers at Hannah's school are in charge of the well-being classes. ____
7 Hannah says that talking to people you know well about emotional problems can be hard. ____
8 New research suggests that children don't speak in class because they are afraid. ____
9 In Hannah's school, speaking is as important as science. ____
10 The first time Hannah gave her talk, she forgot what she was supposed to say. ____

REVIEW and PRACTICE 7

HOME BLOG PODCASTS ABOUT CONTACT

Guest blogger Hannah talks about her school.

A BETTER SCHOOL

As part of Well-being Week last July, Tom and Sam kindly invited me onto their show to talk about the amazing school that I attend. They've now given me the opportunity to write a blog on the subject. Thanks, Tom and Sam!

What do we mean by 'well-being'? According to the dictionary, well-being is 'the satisfactory state of being happy and healthy'. I'm starting here because my school firmly believes that well-being is absolutely necessary for success. Unless students are happy and healthy, they won't achieve their goals. In other words, children make the best progress when they're feeling positive and confident in their abilities. Now this may not sound very surprising to you and I imagine there are few teachers who'd disagree with this statement. However, many schools treat the health and happiness of their students as an extra subject to be dealt with once the main subjects have been taught. In our school, well-being is every bit as important as English.

And how is this achieved, you ask? Well, the main thing is that all students have regular well-being sessions run by a teacher who is specially trained in the subject. During these sessions, we're encouraged to talk about anything that's making us feel stressed or anxious. The teacher then talks us through ways of dealing with these feelings. From time to time all students suffer but we sometimes can't quite manage to tell the people we're closest to. Sessions like these with someone who's skilled at talking about difficult feelings can make a big difference.

But that's not the only thing that's different (and better!) about our school. A vital life skill (in my opinion) that schools rarely give enough attention to is speaking. A recent study suggested that, on average, children speak for as little as 20 seconds in a typical

45-minute lesson. As a result, a lot of young adults leaving school struggle to express themselves. Our school does things very differently. For us, speaking is a key subject – like science. Discussion is a major part of every lesson, including maths. In addition, in the second half of each term, all students write and learn a five-minute speech by heart on their chosen subject. The first time you give your talk, it's scary. (When I first had to do it, my mind went completely blank!) I can tell you that by the time you leave school, you're pretty good at it!

Finally, on every classroom wall is a list of ten school rules, written by the students. Some of these – be polite, do your best, etc. – you might expect; others you may not. 'Admit to your mistakes,' says number 5, and at 6, 'Keep your promises.' I think you'll agree these are good rules for life!

UNIT 8 The changing media

8A LANGUAGE

GRAMMAR: Using linkers (2)

1 Choose the correct options to complete the sentences.

1 _____ you, I actually enjoy driving.
   a While   b Unlike   c Whereas
2 They were badly delayed _____ all the traffic.
   a since   b as   c as a result of
3 Heavy snow is expected this evening. _____, we're closing our café at 3 o'clock.
   a Therefore   b Due to   c Because of
4 Maria thought he was great fun _____ I found him quite annoying.
   a unlike   b since   c whereas
5 _____ I don't jog or go to the gym, I do walk a lot.
   a As a result of   b Unlike   c While
6 I gave away my trainers _____ I never used them.
   a because of   b since   c due to
7 A number of flights have been cancelled _____ the bad weather.
   a as   b since   c due to
8 Some people find his films really funny _____ others just think they're silly.
   a as   b therefore   c while

2 Choose appropriate linkers from exercise 1 to complete the sentences. There may be more than one answer.

1 The north of the country has lots of mountains and hills _____ the south is fairly flat.
2 Unfortunately, the community centre had to close _____ a lack of money.
3 I stopped going to the yoga classes _____ I had a bad back.
4 _____ I don't like all their policies, I do think they've done good things for the environment.
5 _____ Isabel, I don't spend a lot on clothes.
6 Only two people signed up for the class. _____, we've decided to cancel it.
7 Some roads have been closed _____ the recent flooding.
8 I'm actually quite physically active, _____ the rest of my lazy family!

VOCABULARY: The media

3 Read the statements and (circle) True or False.

1 News that is biased contains facts rather than opinions.   True   False
2 Objective reporting contains opinions rather than facts.   True   False
3 A report that is accurate is true and without errors.   True   False
4 A sensational report is shocking or exciting.   True   False
5 A report that is fair cannot be trusted as it gives only one person's opinion.   True   False
6 Breaking news is information about an event happening now.   True   False
7 A programme or person that is on the air is on TV or on the radio.   True   False
8 Tabloids contain mainly serious reports about important events.   True   False

4 Complete the sentences with the correct form of the media words.

1 The newspaper is planning to introduce a s_____ news service for its financial news.
2 He's really funny – I f_____ him on Twitter.
3 The final episode of the series *Friends* attracted an a_____ of over 50 million.
4 I didn't have time to read the paper – I just looked quickly at the h_____.
5 It was reported in the p_____ that over 20,000 people had attended the demonstration.
6 We don't have the film on DVD so we're going to pay to s_____ it.

PRONUNCIATION: Emphatic stress

5 ▶ 8.1 Listen to the sentences and underline the stressed words. Listen and repeat.

1 Ollie is very sociable, whereas Lucy is quite shy.
2 He was in a car accident a few years ago. As a result, he walks quite slowly.
3 Nadia works very hard, unlike most of her friends.
4 We had to postpone our trip, due to all the snow.
5 I was in hospital at the time. Therefore, I was unable to go to their wedding.

SKILLS 8B

READING: Inferring meaning using related words

THE DIGITAL GENERATION GAP

There are a lot of ¹gloomy observations out there about life in the 21st century, the most negative of these, as a rule, being made by older people. The digital age, they say, is ruining our brains. The fact is that, at this point in time, no one really knows the effect of the digital age on our brains, and that's because nothing like this has ever happened before.

So what are the over-40s - the so-called *digital immigrants - saying? Well, they quote a recent study suggesting that, generally speaking, we young people can't concentrate. With our laptops and phones always to hand, we're so used to accessing several sources of information ²sequentially, one after another, that we're no longer able to give our attention to just one thing. Is there any truth in this? Sorry, I'll think about this one later - my phone's ringing ... ONLY JOKING!

They also report a piece of research that claims that we read information on a screen more quickly than we read text on paper. But surely that's a good thing? Well, not so, apparently, because we read information on a screen so quickly that we fail to ³retain it, remembering up to 20% less than when we absorb it from a book. Ah, but what if reading more quickly allows us to read *more*? No one mentions that, do they?

And what about the claim that we're all sleep-⁴deprived, our bodies lacking the rest that's vital for brain function? We're online half the night, they say, chatting with our friends. Obviously, I can't speak for *everyone* but if *my* friends are up till the early hours, it's because they're *studying*. Exams these days are tough!

But, hey, it's not all bad news! There's one skill that we have that our parents don't. We're so used to dealing with a mass of online information that we're able to ⁵filter out and ignore what's irrelevant and get quickly to the facts that we need. So that's something, I guess!

*sad people who grew up before the Internet, tablets, smartphones, etc. and actually had to learn how to use all this stuff

1 Choose the correct options.
1 What is the author's view of the digital age?
  a He/She is hopeful that it will bring benefits.
  b He/She is worried that it will have negative effects.
  c He/She thinks it is too early to comment.
2 According to older people, why are the younger generation unable to concentrate?
  a They are not in the habit of looking at just one thing.
  b They prefer chatting online with their friends.
  c Their phones never stop ringing.
3 According to the research, what is the problem with reading text on a screen?
  a People generally read it more slowly.
  b People do not usually understand it so well.
  c People do not usually remember it so well.
4 The author admits that young people may lose sleep as a result of
  a being online.
  b chatting with friends.
  c studying.
5 Young people are better than their parents at
  a quickly finding what they need from large amounts of information.
  b remembering very large amounts of information.
  c understanding very large amounts of information.

2 For each of the words below, find a synonym in the same sentence in the text. The synonym may be a word or a phrase.
1 gloomy _____
2 sequentially _____
3 retain _____
4 deprived _____
5 filter out _____

3 Complete the expressions in **bold** in the text below by adding one or two words.

> I limit the amount of time I spend looking at a screen. Obviously, when I'm revising for exams, I spend a lot of time in front of a screen, but, ¹_____ **whole**, I spend no more than two or three hours a day on my laptop and phone. ² _____ **speaking**, I think my generation is aware of the problems that screens can cause with sleep and posture. No one wants to have back or neck problems when they're only eighteen so, ³_____ **rule**, we tend to avoid long periods in front of a computer. There's a lot of information out there advising you to take regular breaks and stretch regularly. I think that, **for** ⁴_____ **part**, this education campaign has been very effective in informing young people about the possible dangers.

8C LANGUAGE

GRAMMAR: -ing forms and infinitives

1 Choose the correct options to complete the sentences.

1. Dan helped me *to fill in / filling in* the form.
2. He worked all morning without *to stop / stopping*.
3. James loves not *having to / to have to* shave.
4. She made him *apologize / to apologize* to Paul.
5. Some days I just feel like *to stay / staying* at home.
6. I ran outside *seeing / to see* what had happened.
7. I'd really recommend *getting / to get* the train there.
8. Oh no! I forgot *bringing / to bring* your book with me!

2 Complete the sentences with the correct form of the verbs in the box.

> try   say   give   get up   go   ask   keep   lose

1. Spending three years at university is expensive so you need _____ that in mind.
2. It's no use _____ to persuade her to change her mind. She's made her decision.
3. I really hate _____ early, especially in winter.
4. Alice offered _____ me a lift to the station.
5. In the end I called David _____ for his advice.
6. I'm not really into _____ to rock concerts.
7. _____ goodbye to her at the airport was sad.
8. Please can I borrow your jacket? I promise not _____ it.

VOCABULARY: Common expressions with *at*, *for*, *in* and *on*

3 Complete the sentences with the expressions in the box.

> at first   for no reason   for once   at once
> in trouble   in doubt   on a regular basis
> on behalf of

1. For over an hour, no one came and then suddenly, everyone arrived all _____.
2. I'm accepting this award _____ my father who, unfortunately, can't be with us today.
3. _____, I thought she was serious, but soon I realized that she was joking.
4. Luca is _____ with his parents because he's been missing classes at college.
5. Greta is almost always late but just _____ she was actually on time this morning.
6. The future of the company is _____ as a result of falling sales.
7. You should try to exercise _____, not just when you feel like it.
8. My two-year-old son keeps hitting other children _____ and this really upsets me.

4 Complete the crossword.

Across

2. The nurse on _____ was very inexperienced. (4)
4. He only works part-time, but at _____ that means he has some money coming in. (5)
6. As a child I always wanted to be in _____ of a car. (7)
8. Today, just for a _____, I decided to cycle. (6)
9. Low land like this is at _____ of flooding. (4)
10. I wrote the names out in alphabetical order, just for the _____ of simplicity. (4)

Down

1. Once in a _____, I go to an art gallery. (5)
2. Rebecca was quite badly in _____ at the time. She owed money to three or four friends. (4)
3. She has a full-time job, three young children and on _____ of that, she has sick parents to care for. (3)
5. On _____, I drink five cups of coffee a day. (7)
7. I think Lara is arriving around midday but I don't know for _____. (4)
8. A war between our nations must be avoided at all _____. (5)

PRONUNCIATION: Unstressed pronunciation of *to*

5 ▶ 8.2 Listen to the sentences. Notice the unstressed pronunciation of *to*. Listen and repeat.

1. It's so strange to think we'll never see her again.
2. I'd love to visit Venice in the spring.
3. I'd like to know how much he paid for the car.
4. In the end we decided to cancel the party.
5. She said she hoped to come back one day.
6. Zara came over to speak to me.

SKILLS 8D

SPEAKING: Expressing annoyance and indifference

1 ▶8.3 Listen to the conversation between Julia and Ian and complete the sentences.

1 What's the _____ of visiting someone who just wants to watch TV all the time?
2 I think it's all _____ being lonely.
3 Yeah, that makes _____.
4 Here's what I don't _____.
5 It's hard to _____ why she's being like this, _____ I'm worried that she's a bit depressed.
6 Yes, I see what you _____.

2 Complete the sentences with *whatever*, *however*, *wherever* or *whenever*.

1 Pablo keeps following me _____ I go.
2 _____ hard I study, I'll never pass these exams.
3 'You really need to stop eating so much junk food.' 'Yeah, _____.'
4 _____ I speak to Maria, she always complains about her job.
5 I'll support her, _____ she decides to do.
6 You should apologize, _____ hard that may be.

3 Match the two parts of the sentences.

1 I see what you mean – ____
2 Yeah, that makes sense, I suppose, ____
3 What's the point of ____
4 I think it's all about ____
5 And you see, here's what I don't get. ____

a watching programmes about other people's problems?
b escaping from your own life.
c it makes that sort of unpleasant behaviour seem normal.
d but I'd really like to watch something else now and then!
e My flatmate's an intelligent person.

4 ▶8.4 Complete the conversation with the sentences in exercise 3. Listen and check.

A My flatmate is crazy about soap operas. Whenever I come home, he's watching them.
B Is that a problem?
A Well, I'd prefer to watch something more interesting. ¹_____
A wildlife programme or a good movie would be so much better. ²_____
How can he enjoy these ridiculous stories?
B Maybe he just wants something easy at the end of a hard day's work.
A Maybe. But another thing I hate is the way the characters speak to one another. I think it must affect people who watch them too much.
B Ah, yes. ³_____
A Exactly. To be honest, I never understand why these programmes are so popular.
B ⁴_____
However stressed you are, you can watch soaps and forget your own problems.
A ⁵_____

5 Write a short conversation between two friends talking about annoying social media posts. Include sentences that clarify how they feel and that show their reactions to each other's comments.

47

8 REVIEW and PRACTICE

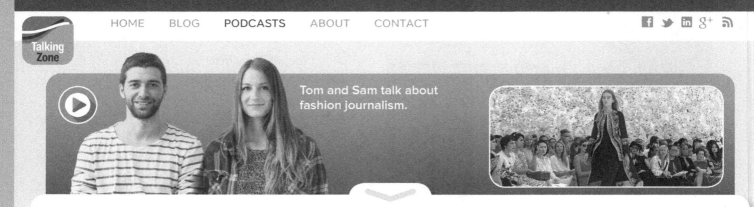

HOME   BLOG   PODCASTS   ABOUT   CONTACT

Tom and Sam talk about fashion journalism.

LISTENING

1 ▶ 8.5 Listen to the podcast and tick (✓) the things Sam, Tom and Hannah talk about.

1 the best stores to go to if you want a great pair of jeans ____
2 how Hannah began her career as a fashion journalist ____
3 her experience of fashion before she became a journalist ____
4 why it's a waste of time to go to fashion college ____
5 the high cost of good-quality clothes ____
6 things about fashion journalism that are different from when she started her career ____
7 how journalists can write about fashion shows even if they haven't been at them ____
8 whether or not she thinks that fashion journalism is a good job ____

2 ▶ 8.5 Listen again and complete the sentences with one or two words.

1 Sam makes a joke about Tom's _____.
2 Hannah says that _____ jeans aren't always the best.
3 Hannah has been a fashion journalist for _____ years.
4 She didn't go to _____.
5 When she was starting, she asked lots of fashion magazines for _____.
6 When she was younger, she worked in a _____.
7 The increase in _____ has changed fashion journalism a lot.
8 Fashion shows are often _____, so you can write about them without being there.
9 Hannah enjoys going to the _____.
10 To have a career in fashion journalism, you need to be an _____.

READING

1 Read Marianne's blog on page 49 and choose the best summary.

a Too much news can have a negative effect on both our physical and our mental health and it is therefore better to avoid it.
b It is important to know what is happening in the world, but we need to be careful that we do not become anxious because of what we read or see.
c News reports focus too much on shocking events and that prevents us from being able to make good decisions.

2 Choose the correct options to complete the sentences.

1 It's so easy to get news that we never think about
   a the quality of news reports.
   b the best places to find accurate reports.
   c the amount of news we watch or read.
2 The media often ignore important issues because
   a they aren't dramatic enough.
   b they prefer to report on bad news.
   c they're too shocking.
3 Video images of news stories
   a give us a better understanding of what has happened.
   b don't usually affect us emotionally.
   c have a more powerful impact on our emotions.
4 If newspapers and news programmes include more happy stories, people
   a suffer fewer negative effects from the news.
   b don't take as much notice of them as the bad news stories.
   c have a better understanding of how to keep themselves safe.
5 It isn't necessary to know what's in the news because
   a it wastes a lot of time.
   b it doesn't help us with our lives.
   c people feel better when they don't know.

48

REVIEW and PRACTICE 8

HOME **BLOG** PODCASTS ABOUT CONTACT

Guest blogger Marianne explains why we should all stop reading the news.

No news is good news!

News is a bit like food – the way we consume it has changed hugely in recent years, and in my opinion it's really not good for us. Like food (in many societies anyway), there's simply too much of it available, and the fact that we can constantly access small amounts means that we end up having far too much – we no longer know when we're full up!

Of course, we all want to know what's going on in the world around us, but relying on news reports certainly doesn't provide an objective view because they over-emphasize events that are dramatic or shocking, whereas other issues are often much more important in reality. So, for instance, the mass media goes crazy if there's a plane crash somewhere while the huge problems caused by stress and anxiety in our modern society rarely make the headlines.

A recent survey by the American Psychology Association found that 1 in 10 Americans check the news at least once an hour and, if you use social media, you can't escape it there, either. Nowadays, anyone can film images on his/her phone, and this means that news often comes to us in a more visual way, which often makes it seem more sensational and upsetting. To go back to the food comparison for a moment, this diet of shocking facts – just like a diet of junk food – can actually be physically harmful. Some researchers suggest that reading bad news on a regular basis can lead to sleep loss, anxiety and even heart disease.

People often say to me, 'Ah, you just need to read some positive stories as well as all the miserable ones,' but I'm afraid our brains don't work that way. We naturally pay more attention to things that frighten us than things we enjoy, which makes sense if you think about it – our ancestors had to be aware of the dangers around them in order to survive.

Personally, I haven't looked at the news for over three years now, and I can't tell you how much better I feel because of that. I sleep better, my concentration has improved, and I can use all that time I used to waste on the news for things that are really important to me. I know it might sound scary to give up altogether, but ask yourself this: when was the last time that anything you read in the news helped you make a better decision or improved your life in any way?

If you can't answer that question, it may be time for you to join my news-free world!

UNIT 9 The power of design

9A LANGUAGE

GRAMMAR: Position of adverbs

1 Put these words in the correct order to make sentences.

1 her / really / Alice / forgetting / friends' birthdays / hates
_____
2 extremely / and / father / was tall / thin / my / mother's
_____
3 cinema / on / got / luckily, / we / time / the / to
_____
4 often / have / I / wondered / she earns / how / her money
_____
5 starting / we / to feel / were / bit / a / tired
_____
6 gave / dollars each / generously / us / my uncle / very / a hundred
_____
7 to arrive / had to / a / I / bit for / the train / wait
_____
8 I / treat / hope I / children / fairly / my
_____

2 Cross out the adverbs that are in the wrong position in this text and insert (^) them in the correct position above the line.

> Some of my friends are jealous a bit of Sophie because she's so good at everything, but I'm not. I just admire her. One of the things I admire really about her is that she's positive amazingly. For example, this year, as well as studying hard incredibly for her exams, she's working in her parents' café. (Her parents can't afford to employ any more staff.) But Sophie is cheerful always and she complains never. I hope she'll be able to a little relax when her exams are over and take perhaps a holiday somewhere nice.

VOCABULARY: Collocations with *have* and *take*

3 Complete the sentences with the words in the box.

| influence | risk | responsibility | argument |
| pleasure | turns | nothing | control |

1 They had an _____ about who should cook dinner.
2 This conflict has _____ to do with religion.
3 You're taking a _____ booking plane tickets this late.
4 I think Sam has a good _____ on his brother.
5 They took great _____ in their grandchildren.
6 She took _____ of the company when her dad died.
7 Millie and I took _____ carrying the heavy bag.
8 We all have to take _____ for our decisions.

4 Read the conversation. Complete each of the phrases with one word.

> A Hey, how did last night go? I hear Paola had you and Jack ¹_____ for dinner?
> B Oh, it was OK, I guess. I went on my own, actually. Jack has a really horrible cold so he had an ²_____ for not going. The evening didn't start so well – I was late as I'd had ³_____ finding Paola's apartment. Then, when I finally got there, I realized it was her birthday. Did you know that?
> A No, I didn't have a ⁴_____! She never mentioned it.
> B That's right. So, of course, I didn't take a card or a present, which was a bit embarrassing. And, stupidly, I drove there. The weather forecast said that it was going to snow, but I didn't take it ⁵_____ – I thought it would be a centimetre at most, not ten centimetres.
> A Oh no! And how did the actual evening go?
> B Well, it just wasn't very relaxing. Paola lives in this perfect apartment – she obviously takes ⁶_____ in every detail – so I spent the entire evening taking ⁷_____ not to spill or drop anything.
> A Oh, dear! That doesn't sound very relaxing.

PRONUNCIATION: Syllable stress with adverbs of degree

5 ▶9.1 Listen to the adverbs. Is the emphasis on the first syllable (1) or the second syllable (2)? Listen and repeat.

1 frequently ___ 4 incredibly ___ 7 truly ___
2 clearly ___   5 carefully ___   8 surprisingly ___
3 amazingly ___ 6 obviously ___   9 remarkably ___

SKILLS 9B

LISTENING: Understanding key points

1 ▶9.2 Listen to Megan interviewing her guest, Lucas, on the radio. Are the following statements true (T) or false (F)?

1 Lucas advises people on what colour to have in their homes. _____
2 Lucas says that the colour red is generally very suitable for homes. _____
3 Megan describes different types of red. _____
4 Lucas recommends orange to people who like warm colours such as red. _____
5 Megan asks Lucas about the colour blue. _____
6 Lucas says blue is always a cold colour, even when it is mixed with other colours. _____
7 Lucas mentions two colours that have blue in them. _____
8 Megan says her bedroom is a calming colour. _____

2 ▶9.3 Listen to some sentences from the interview. Underline the key words that each speaker stresses. (The number of key words is given in brackets.)

1 Red is warm and that can be a good thing, especially in winter. But red also has a lot of energy and it's a colour that gets our attention. (2)
2 It depends on the type of red. (1)
3 I was thinking of a light red – a pinkish-red – rather than a very strong, ruby red. (3)
4 Small amounts can work well inside the house. (1)
5 If you like the warmth of red but want something a little calmer in your home, orange might be the answer. (3)
6 A purplish-blue – violet is also quite warm. (2)

3 ▶9.4 Read the sentences and then listen to the recording. Write ✓ next to the sentence if you can hear the underlined *h* pronounced. Write ✗ if you cannot.

1 Would you like jam on your toast, or <u>h</u>oney? _____
2 The recipe says a teaspoon of salt but I only use <u>h</u>alf. _____
3 I couldn't <u>h</u>ear what Milo was saying. _____
4 Could you take these boxes? They're quite <u>h</u>eavy. _____
5 I called to Dan but <u>h</u>e'd already gone. _____
6 She doesn't like lettuce and she <u>h</u>ates cabbage. _____

4 Solve the anagrams to help you find the colour words.

1 etal = _____: a dark colour that is a mixture of green and blue
2 ovitel = _____: a colour that is a mixture of blue and purple
3 ramono = _____: a colour that is a mixture of red and brown
4 revalden = _____: a light purple colour
5 bury = _____: the dark red colour of a jewel
6 qurutosie = _____: a bright colour that is a mixture of green and blue
7 vrelis = _____: the light grey colour of a metal used in jewellery
8 lodg = _____: the bright yellow colour of a metal used in jewellery
9 robzen = _____: the orange-brown colour of a metal
10 itlucolemourd = _____: having lots of different colours
11 lelywoshi-wronb = _____: the colour of chocolate but with a bit of yellow in it
12 glith = _____: describes a colour that is the opposite of dark

51

9C LANGUAGE

GRAMMAR: Passives and causative *have* and *get*

1 Use the prompts to write sentences using the passive and the tense in brackets.

1 This wall / build / by my grandfather. (past simple)

2 The patients / examine / in this room. (present simple)

3 The motorway / close / this weekend. (future with *will*)

4 He / delay / due to the traffic. (present perfect simple)

5 All the cake / eat. (past perfect)

6 The lab / use / by Class 3BZ. (present continuous)

7 The results of the election / announce / by tomorrow morning. (future perfect)

8 Books / borrow from this library / for up to a month. (*can*, present simple)

2 Rewrite the sentences using causative *have* either in the active or the passive.

1 The hairdresser is colouring my hair this afternoon.

2 Our teacher asked us to do extra homework this week.

3 Someone cleaned our windows yesterday.

4 Someone delivers the shopping to my mum's house.

5 Mr Walker tells us to sing at the start of every school day.

6 My pizza is a bit cold. Could you ask someone to re-heat it, please?

7 Wow, your car looks clean! Did someone clean it professionally?

8 At the workshop, they asked us to list our personal problems.

VOCABULARY: Dimensions and weight

3 Put these units of measurement in order, starting with the least (1).

| mile   inch   foot |

1 _____
2 _____
3 _____

| pint   gallon |

1 _____
2 _____

| ton   ounce   pound   stone |

1 _____
2 _____
3 _____
4 _____

4 Complete the sentences with dimensions and weight words.

1 He w_____ about 180 pounds.
2 These whales can dive to a d_____ of 3,000 metres.
3 This skirt is a little bit short. Can you l_____ it?
4 The room measures 18 s_____ metres.
5 They've w_____ the road to make room for all the extra traffic.
6 He's not short but he's not especially tall. He's probably about average h_____.
7 They've had the river d_____ so that larger boats can use it.
8 This structure supports the w_____ of the ceiling.
9 These shelves are for large books so they'll need to be quite d_____.
10 Tell me the length and w_____ of the room.

PRONUNCIATION: Stress in passive and causative sentences

5 ▶ 9.5 Listen to the sentences. Which of the words is stressed? Listen and repeat.

1 We were told to come here.
2 Most of the food has already been eaten.
3 I'm having my room re-painted.
4 Our flights have been cancelled.
5 Has your bike been repaired?
6 He was questioned by the police.

SKILLS 9D

WRITING: Writing a magazine article

LIVING IN small spaces

1 Many of us live in small flats, sometimes by choice and sometimes not! Although there can be disadvantages to not having much room, it can also be ¹an exciting challenge! Remember, small can be beautiful, and there are lots of things you can do to make your small space work for you.

2 _____
Firstly, you need to think about ²the way you want to live. You might like the idea of lots of stylish, modern kitchen equipment, but if you only cook ³a few times a month, you will probably have to do without it. On the other hand, if your friends call round for coffee most days, you might want to make room for some extra chairs.

3 _____
Many people believe that ⁴small spaces need to be white, but it's surprising how good bright colours can look. If you're not brave enough to paint a wall orange, consider buying a large, colourful painting. Despite what you might think, art isn't only for ⁵the rich – go to local art fairs to find pictures at very reasonable prices.

4 _____
There are several great websites with ideas for small flats. They show photographs of fantastic interior design solutions from ⁶Tokyo to São Paulo. Many of them show creative ways to use ⁷furniture. For example, beds can be raised high off the ground to make room for a desk underneath, and ⁸the desk can be quite large.

5 If you live in a small flat, you really need to make the most of every inch. But, with a little imagination, you can make a home you love.

1 Read the article and match headings a–c with paragraphs 2–4.

 a Look online for ideas
 b Decide what is most important to you
 c Be brave with colour

2 Look at underlined words 1–8 in the article and match them with rules a–h.

 a Use a/an to talk about something/ someone for the first time. ____
 b Use a/an in expressions of frequency. ____
 c Use the before a collective group. ____
 d Use the when something has already been mentioned. ____
 e Use the for something specific. ____
 f Don't use an article before uncountable nouns in general. ____
 g Don't use an article before plural nouns in general. ____
 h Don't use an article before most proper nouns. ____

3 Complete the paragraph with a/an, the or (–).

Last week I visited ¹____ exhibition of ²____ kitchen equipment in ³____ London. ⁴____ exhibition was amazing – I have never seen so many fantastic designs! As a food journalist, I go to ⁵____ exhibitions like this several times ⁶____ year, but this was the best one I've ever seen. They even had a large section of equipment for ⁷____ blind, including things like talking labels for tins. However, ⁸____ thing that impressed me most was ⁹____ fridge that talked.

4 Write an article about something where design is very important. Use one of the ideas in the box, or an idea of your own.

| websites cars fashion magazines parks |

- Give your article an interesting title.
- Introduce the topic in an opening paragraph that readers can relate to.
- Develop your ideas in two or three paragraphs and give each one a heading.
- Summarize your ideas in the final paragraph.
- Pay attention to your use of definite and indefinite articles.

9 REVIEW and PRACTICE

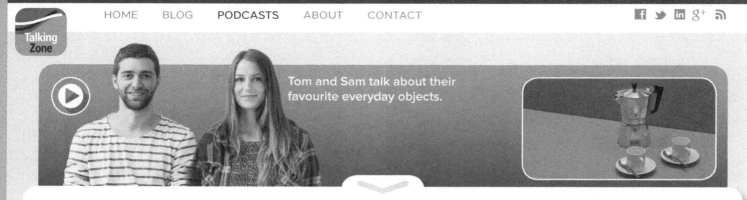

LISTENING

1 ▶ 9.6 Listen to the podcast and tick (✓) the statement which is NOT true.

a Sam's chosen everyday object is not new. ____
b Tom's chosen everyday object is very unusual. ____
c Ethan's everyday object was given to him by a family member. ____

2 ▶ 9.6 Listen again. Complete the sentences with one or two words.

1 Sam and Tom are talking about everyday objects that we _____ great pleasure in.
2 Sam says that Tom takes his coffee _____.
3 Sam wants to know what is _____ about Tom's coffee maker.
4 Tom's coffee maker has _____ very little since it was designed.
5 Sam's favourite everyday objects are her _____.
6 She likes it that you can't see a _____ on them.
7 Ethan's favourite everyday object is a _____.
8 Ethan says he takes great _____ in his handwriting.

READING

1 Read Sam's blog on page 55 and choose the best summary.

a She thinks it's stupid to produce tools that are pink.
b She thinks it's wrong that tools designed for women should be pink.
c She's extremely pleased that her new tool box is pink.

2 Does Sam say these things in her blog? Circle Y (Yes) or N (No).

1 She was surprised to receive a tool box for her birthday. Y / N
2 At the moment, she has nowhere to put her books. Y / N
3 Her friends have already visited her flat. Y / N
4 The company that made her tool box say it's especially for women. Y / N
5 Pink used to be a typically male colour. Y / N
6 There is no reason to produce tools that are light. Y / N
7 She accepts that men's hands are usually larger than women's. Y / N
8 Women have often had trouble using pens designed for men. Y / N

3 Look at the underlined phrasal verbs in Sam's blog. Complete the sentences below with the correct phrasal verbs.

1 They're planning to _____ _____ a new version of this tablet next month.
2 Can you help me _____ _____ the new curtains I've bought for the living room?
3 My uncle always liked to _____ _____ his latest sports car to his friends.
4 Maggie said she would _____ _____ us for dinner one evening next week.
5 This coat doesn't _____ _____ many sizes – only medium and large.

REVIEW and PRACTICE 9

HOME **BLOG** PODCASTS ABOUT CONTACT

In this week's blog, Sam questions the need for 'gendered products', in other words products designed to be sold only to men or women.

Gifts for her ...

My dad recently bought me a box of tools as a birthday present. Yes, I know, it isn't everyone's idea of a nice gift but I'd actually requested it. You see, I moved house last month and now live in an apartment *with no shelves*. I'd love to <u>have</u> my friends <u>over</u> so I can <u>show off</u> my new home but they'd have trouble getting past the *mountain of boxes* in the hall containing all my books. Clearly, I need to do something about this!

Anyway, thanks to my generous Dad, I now have a *lovely* tool box to help me <u>put up</u> some bookshelves. The funny thing is, it's *pink*! And so are the tools inside. Yes, I have a *women's* tool box. OK, it's not *exactly* described this way by the manufacturers. Instead, they refer to it as a 'light tool box, in a fun colour, for small jobs around the house'. But I *think* we know what they mean ...

And how do I feel about this? Well, I'm in two minds. On the one hand, I like pink in all its many shades – light pink, bright pink, dark pink. I wear a lot of pink. Last week, I even had the ends of my hair dyed pink. I don't think there's anything wrong with pink. (And, by the way, until quite recently, there was nothing especially *female* about pink. A hundred or so years ago, it was considered suitable only for men and boys.) To be honest, I probably prefer pink to black, brown, grey or whatever other boring colour tools usually <u>come in</u>. But why should anyone assume that because someone chooses *lighter* tools, they want *pink* tools – or the other way round, for that matter? It certainly makes sense to produce light tools as well as heavy tools so that people who are not amazingly strong can comfortably use them, but I have a suggestion for the makers of tools and tool boxes. Why not produce both heavy and light tools in a range of colours, including pink?

Do you remember those 'pens for women' that were <u>brought out</u> a few years back? The makers said that they were designed to fit the female hand, which is admittedly *generally* a little smaller than the male hand. (Strangely, they seemed not to have noticed that generations of women had for decades been using a pen made for both sexes without experiencing any problems.) I'm guessing I don't need to tell you what *colour* those pens were ...

55

UNIT 10 The business world

10A LANGUAGE

GRAMMAR: Quantifiers

1 Complete the sentences with the words in the box.

| neither | lots | lot | much | none |
| both | few | awful | quite | good |

1 I'm a vegetarian. I have two sisters and _____ of them are vegetarians, too.
2 I'm afraid there's still a _____ deal of work to be done on the apartment.
3 There are _____ of good restaurants in the town centre.
4 Acting is a really tough profession. _____ people succeed at it.
5 There are _____ a few Spanish speakers on the course.
6 A _____ of my time is spent writing reports and keeping records up to date.
7 It's surprising she has red hair since _____ of her parents has red hair.
8 There were six of us for dinner last night so there isn't _____ food left!
9 Sadly, an _____ lot of this packaging is just thrown away.
10 There are several films on TV but _____ of them sound very interesting.

2 Are the underlined quantifiers correct or incorrect? Cross out any mistakes and write the correct quantifiers at the end of the sentences.

1 On such a low salary, there's a little hope that he'll find accommodation that he can afford. _____
2 There are an awful lot of people here tonight. I've never seen this place so crowded. _____
3 Sadly, not much people offered to help the injured man. _____
4 A few politicians are as popular as Sylva. He's very unusual. _____
5 I work with some really great people. I hope you'll meet few of them tonight. _____
6 There's a fair amount of media interest in the subject. _____
7 We had little time to look around the city centre, which we really enjoyed. _____
8 She's taught hundreds of students over the years and she still sees quite a few them. _____

VOCABULARY: Trends and business

3 Complete the sentences by solving the anagrams in brackets.

1 Since 2018 prices have risen _____ (tedasily).
2 Sales of plant-based products have gone up _____ (yarlpsh), almost doubling.
3 Global temperatures continue to _____ (nicaeers) and yet our governments do nothing.
4 The chart shows population _____ (togrhw).
5 Urban populations have _____ (irsne) while the number of people living in the country has _____ (nlafle).
6 There has been a sharp _____ (lalf) in the numbers of EU citizens coming to the UK.
7 Migration has _____ (cdredaese) by 25%.
8 Many of those interviewed complained that their standard of living had _____ (cedlendi).

4 Complete the words in these two texts.

So, I own a ¹c_____ of electrical goods shops. Our ²h_____ office is located here in London and we have 28 ³b_____ in the UK. We sell over two hundred ⁴p_____, most of which are ⁵m_____ in China.

⁶S_____ up a small company is hard. Most small companies go out of ⁷b_____ within their first year. So what problems do ⁸e_____ face when they start up companies? Let's assume that they've come up with brilliant ideas for products they'd like to ⁹l_____ or services they can ¹⁰p_____. Well, the first challenge is to ¹¹r_____ enough money.

PRONUNCIATION: (a) few and (a) little

5 ▶10.1 Read the sentences aloud. Pay attention to how a few, few, a little and little are pronounced. Listen and repeat.

1 She's made quite a few friends since she's been there.
2 I even managed to save a little money last month.
3 Very few people are able to make a living as writers.
4 Life was hard in the war as they had little money.
5 Few animals survive in these harsh conditions.
6 We stopped and had a little food at a roadside café.

SKILLS 10B

READING: Understanding text development

My life as a food delivery cyclist!

Last month I joined the 'gig economy', using my newly purchased road bike to deliver fresh pizza, sushi or ice cream to people in the comfort of their own homes. Depending on your point of view, I'm either:
(a) my own boss, enjoying flexible working hours or
(b) exploited, lacking a contract, holiday pay and protection against accidents.

Well so far, my experience has been almost entirely positive and I'm going with (a)! The job wouldn't suit everyone – for obvious reasons, food delivery cyclists work around meal times when most people see their family or friends. However, my flatmates are chefs and most days they don't get home until midnight. This job means I can fill my evenings usefully, making money and getting fit. What would I do otherwise? Sit on my lonely sofa, staring at a screen? Binge-watch the latest season of some television series?

OK, so it's not the best-paid work. I'm paid £4.50 for every food 'drop'. (I'm not often given tips as my customers have already paid using their phones.) But there are definite benefits. The main advantage is I'm *fit!* I've never exactly been un-fit – I know my way around a gym – but I've never had legs *this* strong. I'm also three kilos lighter while eating chocolate most days – result! And there's another benefit from all this exercise: having cycled fifty miles in the course of a day, I sleep like a log! Finally, there's the job satisfaction I get from providing a useful service. (You should see the happy faces when I turn up at an address with my box of still-hot pizza!)

Of course, the job's not without disadvantages. For example, there's the rain ... on the other hand, it means I do more 'drops'. (No one leaves their home when it's wet.) Worse is the wind – every cyclist's enemy! Also, I sometimes waste time sitting in a restaurant while an order is prepared. That's frustrating, even though some of the friendlier restaurant staff will bring me a drink.

But, overall, I'd recommend it!

1 Are the following statements true (T) or false (F)?

1 For the writer there are more advantages than disadvantages to this type of work. ____
2 The writer says this type of work would not be right for everyone. ____
3 If the writer didn't do this job, she would see her flatmates in the evenings. ____
4 The writer thinks the wages for this type of work are excellent. ____
5 Customers pay the writer when she delivers the food. ____
6 The writer didn't use to be fit before she started this job. ____
7 The writer has lost weight as a result of all the cycling she does. ____
8 The writer mentions one advantage of the rain. ____

2 Circle the words in the second sentences that are connected to the underlined words in the first. Indicate whether the words in the second sentence are related words [REL], reference words [REF], time words [T] or contrast words [C]. The first one has been done for you.

1 She started two <u>companies</u>. Both of (them) were successful.   REF
2 But there are definite <u>benefits</u>. The main advantage is I'm fit! ____
3 For example, there's the <u>rain</u> ... on the other hand, it means I do more 'drops'. ____
4 <u>For example</u>, there's the rain ... on the other hand, it means I do more 'drops'. ____
5 The next few years saw an <u>increase</u> in profits. This rise was caused by two factors. ____
6 <u>Initially</u>, I found him rather cold and distant. Later, I came to like him and very much enjoy his company. ____

3 Complete the second sentence with two words so that it means the same as the first.

1 I've never exactly been un-fit.
  I've _____ quite fit.
2 She had no one to blame but herself.
  She could _____ herself.
3 Her only problem was her lack of confidence.
  Her only problem was that she _____ any confidence.
4 Of course, the job is not without disadvantages.
  Of course, the job _____ disadvantages.
5 Putting up the price of petrol does little to reduce traffic congestion.
  Putting up the price of petrol _____ reduce traffic congestion.

57

10C LANGUAGE

GRAMMAR: Comparison

1 Complete the sentences with the words in the box.

| bit | the | slightly | less | most |
| one | far | as | by | least |

1 _____ more you find out about the case, the more shocking it becomes.
2 Actually, the food wasn't _____ expensive as I'd expected it would be.
3 It was probably the _____ boring talk I've ever heard. I nearly fell asleep.
4 The test was almost impossible. It was _____ more difficult than I'd imagined.
5 I didn't really like the last film. It was my _____ favourite of the three.
6 The good thing is that the more exams I do, the _____ stressful I find them.
7 That was _____ of the best books I've ever read.
8 She was _____ far the best of the dancers.
9 I was a _____ more nervous before the exam than I thought I would be.
10 They're a similar height, but Lara is very _____ taller than her mother.

2 Complete the second sentences so they mean the same as the first sentences.

1 The first and second book in the series were equally good.
   The second book was just _____ the first book.
2 Emily spoke more confidently than any of the other children.
   Emily spoke _____ of all the children.
3 I find that if I start exercising, I want to exercise more.
   I find that the _____, the _____ I want to exercise.
4 Her boyfriend was a little shorter than I was expecting.
   Her boyfriend wasn't quite _____ I was expecting.
5 Klara was more polite than you when she asked for an ice-cream.
   Klara asked for an ice-cream _____ than you.
6 The new exam isn't as challenging as the old one.
   The old exam was _____ than the new one.
7 He ran further than anyone else in his group.
   He ran _____ of anyone in his group.
8 I liked the dessert less than the other two courses.
   Of all the courses, I _____.

VOCABULARY: Word pairs

3 Match the two parts of the sentences.

1 I've seen Maria once ____
2 You'll have to tell him sooner ____
3 He's always making this mistake and I tell him each ____
4 Every marriage has its ups ____
5 He never helps out and I'm sick ____
6 She complains about the same things over ____

a or later.
b and every time.
c and tired of it.
d and over.
e or twice here.
f and downs.

4 Complete the word pairs in the text.

I moved to London from a small village at the start of last year and, by and ¹_____, it was a very good decision. I enjoy living side by ²_____ with people from all different backgrounds – it makes life so much more interesting. Of course, there are pros and ³_____ to any big change that you make in life. I love all the possibilities that a big city has to offer, but, on the other hand, now and ⁴_____ I do miss the ⁵_____ and quiet of the village where I used to live. For example, for the first few weeks of living here, I couldn't get to sleep because of all the noise outside in the street but, little by ⁶_____, I got used to it and now it doesn't bother me at all.

PRONUNCIATION: Sentence stress with *the ... the* comparisons

5 ▶10.2 Underline the stressed words in each sentence. Then read the sentence aloud. Listen and check.

1 It seemed like the more I read on the subject, the less I understood!
2 The more she told me about the job, the more terrifying it sounded.
3 The harder I tried to please her, the less she liked me.
4 The more you research this area, the more fascinating it becomes.
5 Certainly, the more projects I manage, the easier it becomes.
6 The less Anna knows about the situation, the better.

58

SKILLS 10D

SPEAKING: Discussing pros and cons

1 ▶ 10.3 Listen to the conversation between Ana and Marco. Choose the best endings for the sentences.

1 Marco has to decide whether to
  a take a job in another city or not.
  b move to a bigger company or not.
2 He is attracted to the new job because of
  a the money and the increased responsibility.
  b the chance to work in a bigger team.
3 He is worried about the move because he
  a doesn't know anybody in Quito.
  b enjoys the social life he has in Cuenca.
4 Ana suggests that he could
  a only spend Monday to Friday in Quito.
  b invite his friends to stay with him in Quito.

2 ▶ 10.3 Complete the phrases Marco uses to discuss the pros and cons of his decision. Listen again and check.

1 I can't _____ whether to take it or not.
2 One of the _____ of being here is that most of our major clients are in Quito.
3 Each option has its _____, so it's really hard to decide.
4 I'm _____ wanting the challenge of a more senior job and wanting to carry on as I am.
5 One minute I'm _____ going, and the next minute I think I should stay.

3 Use your own ideas to complete the conversations.

1 A What are you planning to do when you leave university?
  B I'm not sure. I can't make up my mind whether to _____.
2 A Have you decided what sort of job you want to apply for?
  B I'm leaning _____.
3 A Are you going to complain about your colleague's behaviour?
  B I'm torn between _____.
4 A Have you thought about getting a job in a different department?
  B I'm not sure. One of the drawbacks is _____.

4 Use the phrases in the box and include some ideas of your own to complete the conversation.

| I really sympathize   look on the bright side |
| you could always   don't let it get you down |

A I'm finding it really difficult to work with the boss I have at the moment. I'm torn between looking for another job and hoping she'll leave soon – she's said that she wants to move to Mexico.

B (Express sympathy.)
_____

A I'm leaning towards leaving, but I was happy before I had to work with her. She's not unpleasant – it's just that we have completely different ideas about how to do things.

B (Make a suggestion.)
_____

A That's certainly something to think about. One of the drawbacks of giving up this job is that I'd probably have to move – there aren't many companies around here that do the same kind of work.

B (Show the positive side of the situation.)
_____

A Yes, you're right. I should try to be positive, but it's difficult and it's so hard to decide what to do. Each option has its pros and cons.

B (Try to cheer A up.)
_____

59

10 REVIEW and PRACTICE

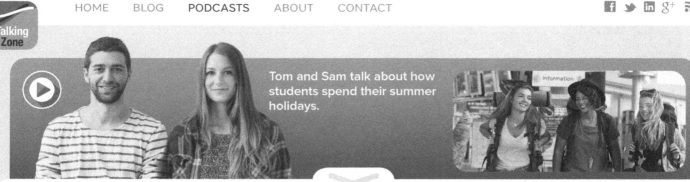

HOME   BLOG   PODCASTS   ABOUT   CONTACT

Tom and Sam talk about how students spend their summer holidays.

LISTENING

1 ▶ 10.4 Listen to the podcast. Choose the correct options to complete the sentences.

1. Zac feels that getting work experience is *fairly / extremely* important.
2. Melissa has a *similar / very different* view.
3. Melissa *has done some / hasn't done any* work experience in her holidays.
4. Tom *approves / doesn't approve* of her attitude.
5. Tom agrees with *Zac / Melissa*.
6. Sam agrees with *Zac / Melissa*.

2 ▶ 10.4 Listen again. Who says these things?

	Zac	Melissa	Nobody
1 I worked for two different companies during my holidays.	___	___	___
2 I managed several restaurants.	___	___	___
3 When you apply for a job these days, there are always a lot of other applicants.	___	___	___
4 It's impossible to get a job without work experience.	___	___	___
5 It's a good idea to spend your holidays doing things you enjoy.	___	___	___
6 Employers aren't likely to choose someone who prefers fun to work.	___	___	___
7 Activities other than working can also be valuable.	___	___	___
8 I intend to do some unpaid work.	___	___	___
9 Most students don't have enough money to be able to work without being paid.	___	___	___
10 Young people shouldn't work all the time.	___	___	___

READING

1 Read the blog on page 61. Match paragraphs A–F with sentences 1–8. There are two sentences you do not need.

1. This company uses a clever trick to assess an applicant's attitude towards other people. ___
2. This company pays their staff very well. ___
3. Many employees want to be able to vary their working hours from time to time. ___
4. Tom's friends are not as happy at work as he is. ___
5. This company gives employees time off to do other things. ___
6. This company employs people who have studied creative subjects. ___
7. This company does a lot to make sure its employees are happy. ___
8. People work better when they feel fit. ___

2 According to Tom's blog, are the sentences true (T), false (F) or doesn't say (DS)?

1. Tom has similar problems to the friends he went out with. ___
2. He likes the idea of judging job applicants by how they treat their taxi driver. ___
3. Employees at Google have to work extremely hard. ___
4. Google staff have the freedom to try out their own ideas. ___
5. The facilities provided by Google help improve the home lives of its workers. ___
6. Employees do not achieve as much if they spend time exercising. ___
7. Providing flexible working hours is very difficult for employers. ___
8. Tom's cousin's firm allows employees to take time off whenever they want to. ___

REVIEW and PRACTICE 10

HOME **BLOG** PODCASTS ABOUT CONTACT

Tom writes about what makes a great workplace.

A happy worker is a good worker

A Last week I went out with a couple of friends and both of them spent the whole evening complaining about their jobs. I felt a bit left out because I love my work, and it got me thinking about just what makes the difference between a job you force yourself to do because you need the money and one you genuinely enjoy.

B Obviously, colleagues have a lot to do with it, and I'm so lucky with mine. (Are you reading this, Sam?) I once heard about a company that always provides a taxi for people attending job interviews. The applicants don't know it, but the driver is a company employee who reports back on their behaviour – the ruder they are, the less likely they are to get a job. That's their way of looking for staff who will treat everyone with respect, and I think it's really cool!

C Apparently, Google has been voted the best place in the world to work several times. Workers say this is because their work satisfies them: it's creative, they can experiment with new ideas, and staff cooperate well rather than competing with one another. In addition, the company puts a great deal of effort into creating a pleasant environment, and one that encourages a good work-life balance, for instance, by providing healthy meals as well as sports, childcare and even laundry facilities.

D Of course, any job can have its ups and downs but there's an awful lot of evidence to show that when employees exercise, they are happier and more efficient and production increases. (Fancy a quick jog before our next podcast, Sam?) Quite a few companies now recognize this by providing exercise classes and gym equipment or by contributing towards the cost of a gym membership.

E However, while all of these benefits are welcome, employees often say that the most valuable thing for them is the opportunity for flexible working. In other words, if you need to go home early one day because the electrician is coming, you can work for longer on other days and not have to use up your holiday.

F Some firms also have schemes that allow employees to follow bigger dreams. My cousin's employer, for example, has something they call 'Five at Five', which means that when you've worked there for five years, you can take five weeks off to travel, work on your novel, build a new room on your house or whatever you want to do. I love that idea, because everyone needs a change now and then. Maybe my dissatisfied friends should go and work there!

61

UNIT 11 Fact and fiction?

11A LANGUAGE

GRAMMAR: Present and past modals of deduction

1 Choose the correct options to complete the sentences.

1 You've made so much food, Isabel! You _____ ages cooking yesterday!
 a might have spent b must have spent c spent

2 Lucy _____ still be at work but I'm not sure.
 a might b can c must

3 I don't know the guy that Julia is speaking to. He _____ be her brother or maybe just a friend.
 a can b could c must

4 Joe isn't answering his phone. He might _____ a film.
 a watch b watching c be watching

5 Daniel _____ told her. That explains it!
 a must have b could have c might have

6 Ethan wasn't even there last night so it _____ have been him that you spoke to.
 a may not b mightn't c can't

2 Rewrite these sentences with modal verbs of deduction. Sometimes more than one option is possible.

1 There's no chance that Paolo has finished all that work already.
   _____

2 It's possible that she's working this evening.
   _____

3 I think I saw her yesterday, but I'm not sure.
   _____

4 Surely I told you the news! I'm sure I did!
   _____

5 She's definitely his mother. She's far too old to be his sister.
   _____

6 It's not possible that she's his child. Sam doesn't have any children!
   _____

7 I don't know why Maria was late this morning. Perhaps she missed the bus.
   _____

8 You know every dish on this menu, Johnny. You definitely come here a lot!
   _____

VOCABULARY: Science

3 Complete the sentences with science words.

1 The study of the human mind is called p_____.
2 The l_____ is the system of rules in a country.
3 E_____ is the study of the production, distribution and consumption of goods and services.
4 A_____ is the study of people from a long time ago by looking at their buildings, tools, etc.
5 G_____ is the scientific study of the Earth's structure and how it was formed.

4 Complete the crossword.

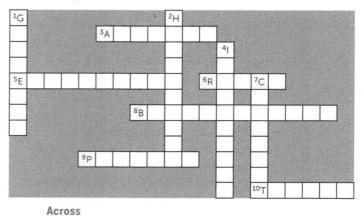

Across

3 Once you've got your data, you need to _____ it. (7)
5 The children did an _____ in the lab. (10)
6 They were unable to _____ a conclusion. (5)
8 There's been a _____ in cancer research. (12)
9 She's going to _____ the results in a journal. (7)
10 That research allowed him to prove his _____. (6)

Down

1 Darwin _____ data about the natural world. (8)
2 He made a fascinating _____. (10)
4 She's _____ a problem she wants to research. (10)
7 He wants to _____ research into dyslexia. (5, 3)

PRONUNCIATION: Reduction of past modals

5 ▶11.1 Read the sentences aloud. Pay attention to the way that *have* is pronounced /əv/. Listen and repeat.

1 I suppose it could have been Sophie.
2 Surely, he must have seen your reply.
3 He might already have told her.
4 You must have heard of him!
5 They can't have arrived already!

62

SKILLS 11B

LISTENING: Identifying conclusions

1 ▶11.2 Listen to Scott and Paloma's conversation and choose the correct options.

1 Who believes there will be a lot of snow next week?
  a Paloma
  b Scott
  c Paloma and Scott's friend, Sarah

2 Paloma says
  a it never snows where they live.
  b it only snows a little where they live.
  c it often snows where they live.

3 Sarah told Scott that
  a an actress sometimes pretends to be the president's wife.
  b the president is married to an actress.
  c the president does not have a wife.

4 Paloma thinks that the story about the president's wife is
  a surprising, but possible.
  b very likely.
  c extremely unlikely.

5 Paloma says that news stories about food
  a change all the time.
  b are usually accurate.
  c are never accurate.

6 Paloma says that people should not repeat stories
  a they have read online.
  b relating to food.
  c without making sure they are true.

2 ▶11.2 Listen again. Complete the phrases that the speakers use to show that they are reaching a conclusion.

1 I mean, _____ items in the news are true.
2 It's _____ which of these 'facts' is true.
3 But before you go repeating it to all your friends, _____, *as far as you can tell*, it's true.
4 Yeah, I guess _____ part of the problem.
5 And _____ false stories about people can really hurt them.

3 ▶11.3 Listen to these sentences and phrases from the conversation and circle the glottal stops..

1 Ah, that doesn't even *sound* believable, does it?
2 Sarah says it's not actually the president's wife.
3 Yeah, I guess if you don't do that, then you're just part of the problem.
4 I know we're laughing about Sarah, but it *is* a serious problem.

4 Choose the correct adjective and add the prefix *un-*, *il-* or *ir-* to give it the opposite meaning.

1 For most people, being separated from your children for several months would be completely _____*imaginable*. / _____*controversial*.
2 The service in the hotel was rather slow and _____*satisfactory*. / _____*responsible*.
3 The problem with the book was that the main characters were _____*acceptable*. / _____*believable*. They didn't behave like anyone I'd ever met.
4 By law, they can't refuse to employ you because you're female. It's _____*legal*. / _____*responsible*.
5 These medicines can have _____*impressive* / _____*desirable* effects on some patients, such as problems with sleeping.
6 Most parents would agree with the statement that raising children is difficult at times. That's fairly _____*controversial*. / _____*satisfactory*.
7 This small, grey building looks rather _____*believable* / _____*impressive* from the outside.
8 No one should be so rude to their colleagues. It's completely _____*acceptable* / _____*legal* to behave so badly at work.
9 It seems rather _____*responsible* / _____*believable* to leave such a young child alone in the house.

63

11C LANGUAGE

GRAMMAR: Reported speech patterns

1 Choose the correct options to complete the reported speech sentences.

1 'I annoyed Rebecca with my comments.'
   She *told / said* that she *has / had* annoyed Rebecca with her comments.

2 'I've been very busy with my coursework.'
   Sam explained *me / to me* that he *had been / was* very busy with his coursework.

3 'I could meet you and Sara a bit later.'
   He said he *could / had been able to* meet us a bit later.

4 'I've been seeing a bit more of Tom recently.'
   He *said / told* me that he *had seen / had been seeing* a bit more of Tom recently.

5 'By next summer, I will have saved up enough to go travelling.'
   Milo *said / said us* that by next summer he *would save / would have saved* up enough to go travelling.

6 'Don't forget to take your passport!'
   My mum reminded me *to take / take* my passport.

7 'When did you take the exam?'
   James asked *me / to me* when *did I take / I took* the exam.

8 'Elephants are the only animals that can't jump.'
   Freddie claimed that elephants are the only animals that *can't / couldn't* jump.

2 Read what Sophia said. Then complete the reported speech sentences with the correct information.

> 'Have you heard the news about David and me?'
> 'I can't afford to go on holiday this year.'
> 'I've been going to yoga classes recently.'
> 'I'm feeling a bit stressed about my exams.'
> 'You really must try Café Blanco!'
> 'You absolutely mustn't mention the party to James.'

1 A Did she mention David at all?
   B Well, she just asked _____ David and her.

2 A Is she going away this summer?
   B No, she said _____ this year.

3 A Is she doing any form of exercise at the moment?
   B Yes, she mentioned _____ yoga classes recently.

4 A Is she calm about her exams?
   B Not really. She said _____ them.

5 A Did she recommend anywhere to eat?
   B Yes, she urged _____ Café Blanco.

6 A Did she say anything about her party?
   B Yes, she forbad _____ to James.

VOCABULARY: Sleep

3 Read the sentences and circle True or False.

1	People often oversleep at the weekend, when they don't have work.	True	False
2	If you snore, you breathe noisily while you're asleep.	True	False
3	People never intend to sleep in. It happens by accident.	True	False
4	People who sleepwalk don't know that they're doing it.	True	False
5	You often yawn when you're tired or bored.	True	False
6	Someone who's sleepy is fast asleep.	True	False

4 Complete the sleep phrases in the text.

Ever since I moved to the city centre, I've been having real problems sleeping. I just can't get used to the noise from the street. Most nights, it ¹_____ me awake until two or three o'clock in the morning. I'm getting three or four hours of sleep a night, which just isn't enough. In fact, I'm so sleep-²_____, I find it hard to ³_____ awake in the daytime when I'm at work. Just this afternoon I nearly dozed ⁴_____ in a meeting. It's so embarrassing! A colleague of mine recommended that I take a ⁵_____ when I get home – just half an hour or so while it's still quiet enough outside. The problem is that if I sleep when I get home, I find I can't ⁶_____ asleep at bedtime. Arghh!

PRONUNCIATION: /t/ and /d/

5 ▶ 11.4 Listen to the sentences. Underline when /t/ and /d/ are fully pronounced. Listen and repeat.

1 He asked me to wait until he'd finished working.
2 They told us it had rained a lot the day before.
3 I urged her to reconsider but she said it was too late.
4 When I reminded her she promised to call him.
5 Tom mentioned that he wanted to go travelling.
6 She asked us to lend her some money.

SKILLS 11D

WRITING: Writing a personal recommendation

Dear Ms O'Reilly

Alex Chambers has asked me to recommend him for a summer job at your riding school, and it is with pleasure that I do so. Alex is a friend of my own son and I first met him when they started school together – around 15 years ago. I run a large farm, and Alex has often worked for me at weekends and in the school (now university) holidays.

Alex is an extremely ¹_____ man. His ²_____ manner has helped him to develop a good relationship with all the animals on our farm. However, it is clear that he has a particular love of our three horses and he spends a lot of time with them even when he is not working. Alex is one of the most ³_____ people I have ever met. He once sat up all night with a sick cow even though he had lectures the next day.

Alex also has ⁴_____ skills. He gets on well with everyone he meets and is always polite and cheerful. Last month, a group of schoolchildren visited our farm and I asked Alex to help with them. I was impressed with the way he looked after the children and answered all their questions, and I am confident he would work well with the young people who come to your school.

Over the last few years, Alex has been an ⁵_____ member of the farm's team and I would not hesitate to recommend him to work for you. If you have any other questions, please feel free to contact me on the number below.

Yours sincerely

Jack Bussell

0121 496 0999

---

1 Read Jack Bussell's personal recommendation and complete the gaps with the pairs of adjectives below.

   a excellent personal
   b calm, patient
   c energetic, reliable
   d pleasant young
   e hardworking, dedicated

2 Read Jack Bussell's personal recommendation again and answer the questions.

   1 How long has Jack known Alex? _____
   2 How did they meet? _____
   3 What example does Jack give of Alex's hard work? _____
   4 What adjectives does he use to describe Alex's excellent personal skills? _____
   5 How should Ms O'Reilly contact Jack if she needs to? _____

3 Is the order of adjectives and the use of commas correct or incorrect in these sentences? Cross out any errors and write the correct version below. Tick (✓) the correct sentences.

   1 His easy-going positive personality would be perfect for this job. _____

   2 She is able to understand financial complicated information. _____

   3 She worked for a Japanese small company that designs websites. _____

   4 He acts in a confident, professional way at all times. _____

   5 She knows a lot about the fascinating, historic city. _____

   6 He would enjoy working in a rural peaceful environment. _____

   7 She is an expert in modern German literature. _____

   8 He is a thoughtful intelligent person. _____

4 Think of a holiday job and someone you know who would do it well. Write a personal recommendation.

   • Explain how you know the person.
   • Describe the person's qualities and give examples.
   • Offer to provide more information.
   • Include at least three pairs of adjectives of opinion and fact and make sure they are in the correct order.

65

11 REVIEW and PRACTICE

Tom and Sam talk about homeopathy.

LISTENING

1 ▶ 11.5 Listen to the podcast and number a–e in the order that you hear them (1–5).

a Sam's friend's snoring problem ____
b Tom's opinion of homeopathy ____
c Scientific experiments ____
d Sam's sister's sleeping problem ____
e a definition of homeopathy ____

2 ▶ 11.5 Listen again and choose the best options to complete the sentences.

1 Tom says he and Sam had been having
   a a chat.
   b a discussion.
   c an argument.
2 Sam says she and Tom had been having
   a a chat.
   b a discussion.
   c an argument.
3 Tom thinks that homeopathy
   a can make you ill.
   b works for some illnesses.
   c is useless.
4 Sam's sister found that she was
   a falling asleep during the day.
   b awake during the night.
   c unable to get to sleep.
5 Sam describes a time when she couldn't sleep because
   a of her lifestyle.
   b she didn't have enough pillows.
   c her friend was snoring so loudly.
6 Tom thinks that people sometimes get better when they
   a believe that a medicine will help them.
   b have someone to talk to.
   c can choose their medicine.

READING

1 Read Sam's blog on page 67. What is her opinion of virtual reality?

a She approves of it and thinks it will have many uses.
b She thinks it is too soon to judge whether it is a good thing.
c She does not approve, especially in relation to its effect on the brain.

2 According to Sam's blog, are the sentences true (T), false (F) or doesn't say (DS)?

1 Some people are worried about virtual reality. ____
2 People wearing virtual reality headsets sometimes have accidents. ____
3 Our brains understand that a virtual reality experience is different from a real experience. ____
4 A virtual reality experience may have a physical effect on the body. ____
5 Sam hasn't been to many art exhibitions. ____
6 Sam is often bored at art exhibitions. ____
7 Modigliani lived to an old age. ____
8 The studio was Modigliani's home as well as his place of work. ____

3 Look at the underlined words in Sam's blog. Complete the sentences below with the correct words.

1 When I was in London I saw an amazing _____ of Roman sculptures at the British Museum.
2 When he realized that the dog wasn't tied up, his heart started to _____.
3 The Uffizzi Gallery in Florence is full of wonderful _____ of _____ from the fifteenth and sixteenth centuries.
4 When people feel tired or bored they often _____.
5 At that time he was a _____ artist – he wasn't well-known and he had very little money to live on.

66

REVIEW and PRACTICE 11

HOME **BLOG** PODCASTS ABOUT CONTACT

This week, Sam finds that virtual reality helps her to appreciate art as never before …

Reality, but not as you know it!

There's a degree of public concern these days about the use of virtual reality — that is, artificial places and experiences produced by computers that feel *like* reality to the person experiencing them. Of course, there's the obvious danger of the VR user being blind to the real world around them when they're wearing a headset. (People using VR headsets can knock into and fall over physical objects if they're not watched and carefully guided by others!)

Then there's the more worrying question of what effect VR has on the brain. After all, psychologists tell us that the brain experiences virtual reality as *actual* reality. Our body responds to a VR experience exactly as if we were really having a *real-life* experience, for example fear causing our breathing to become quicker or our heart to pound. Surely, this can't be good for the brain? It must be confusing, to say the least. Well, like all very recent inventions and developments, we don't yet know what the long-term effects will be. Only time will tell …

In the meantime, VR is out there and, after this weekend, I can tell you from personal experience that it can be put to *amazing* use. My friend, Sarah — a big fan of the painter Modigliani — took me to see an exhibition of his work at the Tate Modern gallery. Now, don't judge me, but I'm not a huge fan of art exhibitions and quite often find myself yawning as I look at picture after picture. This, however, was an exhibition with a difference — I wasn't bored for one second. There was, of course, an extensive display of the artist's paintings but there was also a VR recreation of Modigliani's Paris studio — an unimpressive, narrow room, 'reimagined' in unbelievable detail. Wearing a VR headset, we 'stepped into' that studio and looked around the room where he painted in the final months of his short life.

Leaning against the walls were beautiful works of art, some completed, some not. The artist's brushes and tubes of half-used paint lay where he'd left them — I felt as if I could *smell* the paint drying — and an unfinished cigarette burned away in an ashtray. The room was dark, an open window letting in a little light, and a mattress lay on the floor. Clearly, the struggling Modigliani must have lived here as well as worked here. Talk about confusing VR with real-life experiences — I got such a strong sense of actually *being* in the studio that I felt that Modigliani might at any point walk into the room and ask me what on earth I was doing there! Having 'visited' the place where the works of art were created, I then found myself unexpectedly fascinated by the exhibition of his paintings. If only every art exhibition had a VR element!

67

UNIT 12

New discoveries

12A LANGUAGE

GRAMMAR: Present and future unreal conditions

1 Complete the sentences with the words in the box.

| could | time | only | rather |
| would | wish | if | were |

1 If I earned more money, I _____ afford to buy a car.
2 I love the sea. If _____ I lived near the coast.
3 If I _____ you, I'd tell him how you feel.
4 I _____ I could sing as well as you.
5 I _____ look for a new job if I were you.
6 He's thirteen now. It's about _____ he started helping out around the house!
7 It's a private matter. I'd _____ you didn't tell anyone else about it.
8 _____ only I had enough money to give up work.

2 Complete the sentences with the correct form of the verbs in the box. Use one verb twice.

| not live | spend | buy | be able |
| be | have | speak |

1 I'd love to go surfing more. If only I _____ more free time.
2 If you didn't spend so much money going out all the time, you _____ save up for your holiday.
3 I'm so sad. I wish you _____ here with me.
4 I don't understand. I wish I _____ Spanish.
5 I'm sure Joe would happily spend all day on his laptop, but I'd rather he _____ time with his friends.
6 Why are his parents still buying his clothes? At 31, it's about time he _____ his own clothes!
7 She's bored. She wishes she _____ in a village.
8 Sarah _____ a bit more money if she were prepared to work a few more hours!

VOCABULARY: Phrasal verbs (2)

3 Match the two parts of the sentences.
1 Yesterday Alan's car broke _____
2 I've forgotten my password so I can't sign _____
3 I can't figure _____
4 I can't make you a sandwich because we've run _____
5 Why don't you note _____
6 You should just hang _____

a out of bread.
b up if he phones you again.
c down on his way to work.
d out what's wrong with my phone.
e in to my social media account.
f down his telephone number?

4 Complete each pair of sentences with the correct forms of the same phrasal verb.
1 a I've looked everywhere for that book but I can't find it. I'm hoping it will just _____ _____.
   b I love this song. Could you _____ it _____, please?
2 a When you make a statement in an essay, you need to _____ it _____ with evidence.
   b You really don't want to lose your work so make sure it's _____ _____ on a USB drive.
3 a She's been _____ _____ a hard time recently with health problems and difficulties at work.
   b I've just _____ _____ the drawers in my desk but I can't find that letter anywhere.
4 a We've _____ _____ a meeting to discuss the problem.
   b I need ten minutes to _____ _____ the laptop.
5 a The salary's higher so he won't _____ _____ the job.
   b Could you _____ your music _____, please?
6 a Hey, guess who I _____ _____ in town?
   b The project started well but then we _____ _____ a few difficulties.

PRONUNCIATION: Consonant-vowel linking

5 ▶12.1 Read the sentences aloud. Underline any consonant-vowel linking in each sentence. Listen and check.
1 Can I borrow this pen, please?
2 He asked Alice to get a plate from the kitchen.
3 Did Andrea buy a ticket for the show?
4 Could Oliver come along with us this evening?
5 When Isabel was a little girl, she had a dog.
6 Is it OK if I take this chair?

SKILLS 12B

READING: Predicting

More plastic than fish?

The oceans of our planet are full of plastic and we have no one to blame but ourselves. Shockingly, we dump the equivalent of a lorry-load of plastic into our oceans every minute of every day. If this carries on, by 2050 there will be more pieces of plastic in our oceans than fish. This is, of course, a disaster for all of us – wildlife and humans alike. Indeed, it is claimed by some environmentalists that plastic pollution in our oceans is as serious a problem as climate change. Clearly, we urgently need to do something about it.

Fortunately, there are some brilliant people out there using new technologies to develop tools that will help tackle this very serious problem. Two Australian surfers have invented a device called the SeaBin, a floating rubbish bin that sucks rubbish off the water's surface. (The same device also removes oil.) Another potentially brilliant invention by a young Dutch engineer, Boyan Slat, aims to collect half of the plastic rubbish in the Great Pacific Garbage Patch within five years. (The Great Pacific Garbage Patch is a huge pile of floating rubbish – twice the size of France – in the Pacific Ocean.)

Other brilliant innovations include an instrument that can be attached to a ship that measures plastic pollution as the ship moves along. Theoretically, the data gathered by this instrument will allow us to work out how the plastic is moving and exactly where it is ending up. This, in turn, will help us to deal with the problem.

Obviously, inventions like this won't completely solve the problem of plastic pollution in our oceans. As a matter of urgency, we humans need to change our behaviour. We must use far less plastic, finding alternatives to the plastic bottles and bags that find their way into our rivers and oceans in their millions. And we must find cost-effective ways to recycle what we do use. In the meantime, we should all be extremely grateful to these inventors and support their efforts in any way we can.

1 Read the first paragraph only of the text and predict (✓) which of these summaries best describes the whole of the article.

a Which is more damaging – climate change or plastic pollution? _____
b The drastic fall in the number of fish in our oceans. _____
c The serious problem of plastic pollution and new ways to solve it. _____
d How climate change is affecting our oceans. _____

2 Tick (✓) the statements that are true.

1 We use lorries to put plastic into our oceans. _____
2 There are now more pieces of plastic in our oceans than fish. _____
3 Some people are as worried by plastic pollution as they are by climate change. _____
4 A device has been invented that takes rubbish and oil out of the water. _____
5 Another device has removed half of the plastic rubbish in the Great Pacific Garbage Patch. _____
6 The plastic in our oceans does not stay in the same place. _____
7 Fortunately, we are starting to use less plastic in our daily lives. _____
8 We should do everything possible to encourage people who create devices to deal with the problem of plastic pollution. _____

3 Circle the comment adverb that makes most sense in each sentence.

1 *Shockingly / Understandably*, no one apologized for the terrible way in which she had been treated.
2 This situation is *fortunately / theoretically* possible, although in practice it is highly unlikely.
3 He was *understandably / luckily* upset by the sad news.
4 For a short guy he's *surprisingly / obviously* good at basketball.
5 My train was cancelled. *Understandably / Fortunately*, Steve was able to give me a lift home.
6 It started raining but, *luckily / apparently*, I had my umbrella with me.
7 Lucy and I had a long chat. *Apparently / Theoretically*, Laura has a new job.
8 It was a complete accident so *surprisingly / obviously* no one is to blame.

12C LANGUAGE

GRAMMAR: Past unreal conditions

1 Read the sentences and write T for third conditional sentences and M for mixed conditional sentences.

1 If I hadn't eaten that dessert, I wouldn't feel so full now! ____
2 If she'd worked a little harder, she might have got into university. ____
3 I'd have bought extra food if I'd known you were coming. ____
4 If she hadn't taken so many risks, she would probably still be alive today. ____
5 The steak would have been better if they hadn't cooked it so long. ____
6 He'd look better if he hadn't dyed his hair. ____
7 If you hadn't upset her, she would be here now. ____
8 If we'd set off earlier, we might have reached London by now! ____

2 Complete the sentences with the verbs in brackets in the correct order. Where it says T, write third conditional sentences and where it says M, write mixed conditional sentences.

1 If you _____ me about the problem, I _____ you. (help / tell) **T**
2 If we _____ the train, we _____ there by now. (be / not miss) **M**
3 It's strange to think that if I _____ a different job, I _____ you! (not meet / take) **T**
4 I'm sure I _____ her face if I _____ her. (remember / meet) **T**
5 If I _____ it was a party, I _____ something smarter. (wear / know) **T**
6 If he _____ himself, he _____ so ill now. (not be / look after) **M**
7 You _____ how to use the machine if you _____ the instructions! (read / know) **M**
8 I _____ to the party if I _____ you needed a lift. (know / drive) **T**

VOCABULARY: Collocations with *come*, *do*, *go* and *make*

3 Complete the phrases in the sentences with the correct forms of *come*, *do*, *go* or *make*.

1 She has a new movie that's _____ out later this year.
2 Thankfully, they've _____ away with the old registration system and now it's much easier to sign in.
3 William's never been a hard worker. He just _____ the minimum to pass his exams.

4 As far as I know, she's still _____ ahead with her plans to open up a café in the city centre.
5 I've no idea what she means in that last paragraph. It doesn't seem to _____ any sense.
6 You've got to _____ an effort to get to know people if you want to make new friends.
7 Alice _____ the point that they'll close the community centre unless more people use it.
8 I won't go into details about the plans, but I'll quickly _____ over the main points.

4 Complete the phrases in this email with the correct forms of *come*, *do*, *go* or *make*.

To: Mum
RE: Greetings!

Hi Mum

When I came out here six months ago, it felt like a lifetime in front of me. I can't believe my stay in Africa is ¹_____ to an end. I'd always wanted to work with elephants so when I came here it felt like my dream had ²_____ true. I'll always be grateful to you, Mum, for encouraging me to come here. I wasn't 100% sure I wanted to do it, but you told me to ³_____ for it and pointed out that opportunities like this don't ⁴_____ along every day. You were so right. I've absolutely loved working with the elephants – feeling that I'm ⁵_____ my part to help them survive. It's so sad that people have ⁶_____ such harm to their habitat over the years – they really need all the help they can get. I'm even beginning to think that one day I might ⁷_____ a living from this sort of work. I've been talking to one of the team leaders about how this might happen. I'll ⁸_____ into detail when I see you …

Love, Klara xxx

PRONUNCIATION: Stress in past unreal conditional sentences

5 ▶12.2 Circle the stressed word in the underlined part of each sentence, then read the sentence aloud. Listen and check.

1 I wish Sarah had seen the film, too. <u>She'd have loved it</u>.
2 <u>He might have come</u> if you'd asked him.
3 If I'd been worried, <u>you'd have known about it</u>.
4 <u>You wouldn't have made</u> so many mistakes if you hadn't rushed the essay!
5 If I hadn't been ill that night, <u>I'd have joined you</u>.
6 If I lived a bit nearer, <u>I could have gone</u> to her party.

70

SKILLS 12D

SPEAKING: Talking about future trends

1 ▶ 12.3 Listen to Laura and Adam discussing new technology. Number these phrases in the order that you hear them. Listen again and check.

- a Speaking of … _____
- b … I don't know how many … _____
- c It's a bit like … _____
- d That reminds me … _____
- e … or whatever … _____
- f The thing that looks like … _____
- g You mean …? _____
- h What exactly do you do with it? _____

2 According to Laura and Adam, what:

1 is bound to happen?
_____

2 is conceivable?
_____

3 is anyone's guess?
_____

4 is unlikely to happen soon?
_____

3 Use your own ideas to complete these sentences.

1 One day, someone is bound to invent _____
_____ .

2 In the future, it is conceivable that everyone will be able to _____ .

3 _____ is a fad that isn't likely to last.

4 Whether _____
will be possible in the future is anyone's guess.

4 ▶ 12.4 Use phrases from exercise 1 to complete the conversations. Listen and check.

A Have you seen this phone charger?
¹_____ a credit card.
B ²_____ this thing? You can really charge a phone with something this small? That's amazing! I really need one of these – my phone runs out of charge ³_____ times a week.
A Yes, it's very useful and so easy to carry around. ⁴_____ very small things, I read that there's now a computer that's the same size as a grain of salt.

A What's that on your table?
B ⁵_____ a small music speaker? It's to help to keep my apartment safe when I'm not here.
A ⁶_____?
B You just switch it on in the evenings ⁷_____ time you want, and it makes noises to make people think you're at home.
A That's a good idea.
B Yes, it is. ⁸_____ – I should switch it on now if we're going out.

5 Think of a modern invention and write a short conversation about it.

A (Introduce the topic of the invention.)
_____

B (Ask for clarification.)
_____

A (Describe the invention.)
_____

B (Make a prediction about the invention.)
_____

A (Introduce a new topic in a general way.)
_____

12 REVIEW and PRACTICE

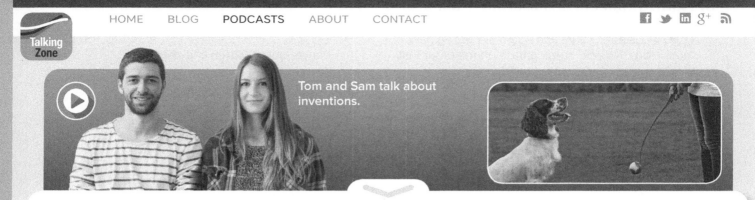

LISTENING

1 ▶ 12.5 Listen to the podcast. Tick (✓) the inventions that Tom, Sam and Lorna mention. Then tick (✓) the inventions that already exist.

	mentioned	already exist
1 dog ball throwers	___	___
2 a house on legs	___	___
3 an electronic insect	___	___
4 windows that make energy from the sun	___	___
5 phones that don't need batteries	___	___
6 phones that can see round corners	___	___
7 artificial skin that can feel things	___	___
8 invisible objects	___	___

2 ▶ 12.5 Listen again and complete the sentences.
1 Tom doesn't like bending down to _____ _____ his dog's ball.
2 He says plastic throwers are a _____, _____ solution to the problem.
3 Lorna's favourite invention is the _____ _____.
4 It can move as fast as a _____.
5 Solar windows in a Dutch bank generate enough electricity for employees to _____ their _____.
6 Smart gloves could be printed using _____ _____.
7 Tom wants to have a _____ that would make him _____.
8 According to Lorna, a _____ of _____ is working on making invisible objects.

READING

1 Read Lara's blog on page 73 and choose the best summary.
a Lara finds it annoying when her parents can't use their phones, but she tries to be patient and help them because she understands that using phones is difficult for older people.
b Lara's parents enjoy making her angry with the way they use their phones because she made them angry when she was a teenager. Lara tries to be patient with them but finds it very difficult.
c Lara finds her parents' struggle to use their phones extremely annoying. She wonders if they are doing it on purpose because she caused them problems when she was younger.

2 Tick (✓) the statements that are true.
1 Lara thinks her parents are too young to find phones difficult. ___
2 Lara's mum knew that her bus was likely to be late. ___
3 Lara thought it should have been obvious to her mum that she needed to have her phone on. ___
4 Lara doesn't think her dad should need help to do things on his phone. ___
5 He usually remembers what to do if she explains carefully. ___
6 Lara's own phone isn't as good as her parents' phones. ___
7 Lara's parents aren't aware of many of the things that their smartphones can do. ___
8 Lara doesn't really believe that her parents are pretending to have problems with their phones. ___
9 She's always nice to them when they ask her for help. ___
10 They're good at texting quickly. ___

REVIEW and PRACTICE 12

HOME **BLOG** PODCASTS ABOUT CONTACT

Guest blogger Lara writes about helping her parents use technology.

Mum, Dad and the modern world ...

If only my mum and dad weren't so useless with their phones! They're not even that old, so they can't use that as an excuse. I'm beginning to suspect that they do it on purpose to annoy me. Maybe it's their way of punishing me for the dreadful time I gave them as a teenager. Whatever the reason, it drives me crazy!

For instance, a couple of weeks ago, I arranged to meet my mum for lunch in town, but my bus got stuck in a traffic jam. I tried and tried to call her, but her phone went straight to voicemail. Then she was really annoyed that I was late, and when I protested that I'd tried to call her, she just said, 'Oh, my phone's not switched on.' So, there she was, wondering what had happened to me and getting angrier and angrier, but it didn't even cross her mind to switch her phone on! Honestly, I give up!

In some ways my dad's even worse. He's always asking me how to do stuff like attaching a photo to an email or turning up the volume. Now, I don't think I've ever in my whole life needed anyone to tell me these things because they're COMPLETELY OBVIOUS! Still, I try (not always successfully!) to explain patiently, and he nods his head and thanks me. But the next time he wants to do them, he's completely forgotten, and I have to go over it all again. And again. And again ...

Another thing that makes me furious is that they both have the latest smartphones – far nicer than anything I can afford – but they could do so much more with them if only they understood them better. For instance, my dad was telling me a story about driving round and round London and being completely unable to figure out how to get to where he wanted to go. When I asked him why he hadn't used his phone, he said, 'My phone has a map on it?' in total astonishment!

Maybe if I hadn't been such an awful teenager, my parents would make more of an effort not to annoy me by being so rubbish with their phones. But, sadly, I think their problems are genuine. One part of me (the nice part!) wishes I could be kinder to them about it, but the less nice part thinks it's about time they moved into the twenty-first century and learned how to use their phones like normal people! And don't get me started on watching them text with one finger ...

WRITING PRACTICE

WRITING: Making a narrative interesting

1 Read Irene's blog post about a scary film. Complete the post with the time linkers in the box. There may be more than one correct answer, but do not use the same linker twice.

> after a while   before long   at first   in a matter of minutes/hours   in the beginning
> to begin with   eventually   in no time   as time went on

1 Last night my friend Elena and I went to see a film called *The Other Child* at the Cinema Royale. I knew it was about a ghost, but I didn't expect it to be too scary. 'My auntie Maria saw it on Monday and she loved it,' I told Elena, 'so it can't be that bad.' How wrong I was!

2 ¹_____, it seemed like any other film. The characters were a little bit weird, but there were several funny moments and people in the audience were laughing. However, ²_____ the laughter stopped. It's hard to explain exactly why, but a feeling of fear was spreading through my body like ice. 'Come on, Irene,' I told myself. 'You know it's just a story.'

3 Suddenly, I realised that as we'd been sitting there, the whole cinema had become colder and ³_____ the lights had been turned down until it was almost completely dark. I could feel my heart banging like a drum in my chest. I didn't say anything to Elena because I thought she'd think I was being silly, but ⁴_____ I noticed that her body was shaking – she was just as scared as me!

4 By this time, the whole audience was silent. We all knew that something awful was about to happen, but when the ghost ⁵_____ appeared on the screen, everyone screamed in shock. Elena turned to me. 'Why did you make me come to this?' she demanded.

5 Afterwards, we went for a coffee to calm down. We agreed it was the scariest film we'd ever seen. Elena said she had enjoyed it, but my legs felt like jelly and I'm not sure I ever want to see a film like that again!

2 Answer the questions.

1 How scary did Irene think the film would be?
2 What did she say about her aunt's experience of the film?
3 How did she describe her feeling of fear?
4 What did she say to herself when she felt frightened?
5 How did she describe the way her heart felt?
6 Why didn't she tell Elena how scared she was?
7 What did Elena say when the ghost appeared?
8 What did Irene's legs feel like after the film?

3 Look at the third paragraph of Irene's post. Which tenses does she use? Now choose the correct tenses to complete the paragraph below.

> Yesterday evening I ¹*had watched / watched* a really interesting programme about the Arctic. The programme makers ²*had worked / were working* for over a year with a group of scientists who ³*researched / were researching* wildlife there. They ⁴*had managed / had been managing* to film a family of polar bears and it was lovely to watch them. However, one of the scientists ⁵*was working / had been working* in the Arctic for over 30 years and he ⁶*explained / had explained* how difficult it can be these days for polar bears to find enough food.

4 Write a blog post about a movie, play or TV programme that turned out to be different from what you had expected.

- Include different narrative tenses and time linkers.
- Use comparisons, predictions and direct speech to make your story more interesting.

WRITING PRACTICE

WRITING: Writing a persuasive article

1 Read the text. <u>Underline</u> the two sentences in which the author gives her general opinion about the value of tidiness very clearly.

Love the mess you live with!

Marie Kondo has written several books about being organized. In her opinion, you shouldn't have anything in your house that doesn't 'spark joy' (in other words, cause great happiness) and she has very strict instructions about things like folding clothes in a way that 'respects' them. Well, in *my* opinion this obsession with being tidy is a complete waste of time.

At first glance, her ideas look simple and easy to carry out. However, my friend Jayne tried them and it took her days and days. Personally, I'd far rather read a book or go out with friends than fold shirts or waste time thinking about whether or not a particular lamp gives me happy feelings.

And as for objects 'sparking joy' – initially, that might seem like a lovely idea, but actually there are several problems with it. Firstly, cost. Who can afford to replace everything they're not totally happy with? Secondly, the environment. No, I don't feel joy when I look at my toaster, but, hey, it makes great toast and it would be wasteful to throw it away.

Thirdly – and most importantly – I don't really approve of spending so much energy on objects.

You might think it would be nice to buy that beautiful set of mugs, but, in fact, it's the *people* who will be drinking coffee with you that really matter. A warm and friendly atmosphere is much more important than having a perfect home.

I'm well aware that Marie Kondo's books have been very popular. I guess everyone's different, but in my view life's too short to spend so much time worrying about how neat and tidy your house is.

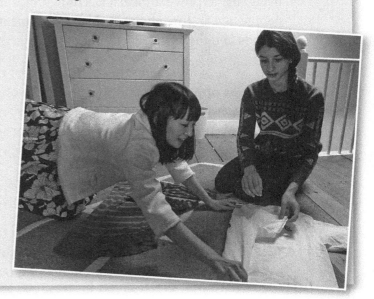

2 The writer does not agree with the idea that every object in a home should 'spark joy'. Tick (✓) the reasons she gives.

1 It's too expensive. _____
2 It's silly. _____
3 It isn't possible for everything to spark joy. _____
4 It isn't environmentally-friendly. _____
5 It isn't good to think about objects so much. _____
6 She doesn't want her home to be perfect. _____

3 How important do you think it is to have a tidy home? State your opinion clearly and give three reasons.

1 (opinion) _____

2 (reason 1) _____

3 (reason 2) _____

4 (reason 3) _____

4 Find these phrases for expectations in the text and <u>underline</u> the words that show the reality of the situation.

1 At first glance, …
2 initially, that might seem …
3 You might think …

5 Write a text about the importance of being tidy.
- State your point of view clearly.
- Give reasons and support them with facts and examples.
- Use persuasive language.
- Include at least two expressions for contrasting expectations with reality.

WRITING PRACTICE

WRITING: Writing an opinion essay

1 Read the essay and add the topic sentences to the correct paragraphs.

a One reason is that in those days people didn't use to have so much pressure in their lives.
b **In sum**, despite the progress of modern years, life is worse now than it was fifty years ago.
c There is no doubt that life is totally different today from how it was for our grandparents when they were in their twenties.
d In addition, we are less active and in many ways less healthy than we were 50 years ago and that is definitely not a good thing.

Is life better today than it was 50 years ago?

1 ^{1}_____ Of course, there has been enormous progress in certain areas of our lives, for example in medical care and communication technology. For example, since 1980 we have been able to prevent measles, a dangerous disease which used to kill around 2.6 million people a year. Inventions such as Skype mean that it is easier than ever to stay in touch with friends and family. **Nevertheless**, I believe that life was better 50 years ago.

2 ^{2}_____ Most families could afford for the woman to stay at home and look after the house, **as opposed to** now, when women often have to go out to work and then do most of the housework as well. **Similarly**, before social media, people didn't have to worry about posting the perfect picture on Instagram or seeing how many 'likes' they could get for their latest selfies.

3 ^{3}_____ Everyone is busier and fast food is available everywhere. **Consequently**, more than two-thirds of adults in the USA are now overweight. So, while we may live longer, our health is likely to suffer.

4 ^{4}_____ We are more stressed and in some ways less healthy and no recent invention – not even the internet – is worth more than our physical and mental health.

---

2 Identify the paragraph or paragraphs in the essay that include the following:

1 dates and figures to support an argument ____
2 arguments to support the thesis ____
3 a thesis statement ____
4 a conclusion ____

3 Look at the linkers in **bold** in the text. Now use them to complete the sentences.

1 We have plenty to eat, _____ our grandparents who were often hungry when they were children.
2 Today we all have washing machines and dishwashers and _____ life is easier.
3 These days, it is much easier to travel. _____, it is easier to keep in touch with friends and family all over the world, for example by Skype.
4 It is true that social media can cause problems. _____, I believe it also has many advantages.
5 _____, I believe that life today is definitely better than it was in the past.

4 Write an opinion essay giving the opposite view to the one in the text.

- Provide a clear thesis statement.
- Start each paragraph with a topic statement.
- Give arguments to support your thesis statement, with examples, facts, figures, etc.
- Summarize the key points in the concluding paragraph.
- Use at least three formal linkers to connect your ideas.

WRITING PRACTICE

WRITING: Writing a set of guidelines

How to write a great blog

Your best friend writes a motor racing blog and your neighbour posts 2,000 words on tropical fish twice a week. But how many of these articles do you read? Probably not many, and yet some bloggers are so successful they have thousands of followers. How do they do it?

Have something unique to say

It's fine to write about the same subject as other people, but you need something original to attract readers to your blog. For instance, there are thousands of fashion blogs, but I always read a particular one about really unusual sports clothing. I'm never going to wear those clothes, but I find the posts interesting. [1]_____, the author has a really nice writing style and a great sense of humour.

A picture is worth a thousand words

Yes, a blog is about writing, but everyone likes a picture. It makes the page look attractive. [2]_____, it can give an instant clue to what the post is about. My friend writes a blog about running and he says that posts with pictures always get more likes and comments.

If a thing's worth doing, it's worth doing well

Always check your work carefully. I was reading a post about money-saving tips recently. [3]_____, it had so many spelling mistakes, I didn't really trust the author's advice. [4]_____, if you want readers to spend time reading your blog, you should respect them by making sure it's correct.

Know your readers

I'll end with my most important piece of advice: familiarize yourself with the people that read your blog. You need a clear idea of who they are. Communicate with them – answer their comments, notice which posts they like best. The best way to get people to come back to your blog is to give them what they want!

1 Read the blog post. Choose the best linker for each gap.

1 *However / Moreover / Similarly*
2 *In addition / Nevertheless / However*
3 *Besides / Moreover / However*
4 *Similarly / Besides / However*

2 <u>Underline</u> the sentences in the blog post in which the author includes an example or a personal experience.

3 Match guidelines 1–5 with reasons a–e.

1 Always make sure you know who can see your social media pages. _____
2 Ignore people who post unpleasant comments. _____
3 Never put your address on a social media site. _____
4 Don't include too much information. _____
5 Never tell anyone your passwords. _____

 a Only people you trust and know well should know where you live.
 b Readers only need to know the basics to begin with.
 c They could post on your pages as a joke or to get you into trouble.
 d You might not want future employers looking at photos of you at parties!
 e If you react, it just encourages them to do it again.

4 Choose one of the topics below and write a blog post giving a set of guidelines.

Staying safe online.
How to get the best from social media.
Helping your grandparents use the internet.

- Write a short introduction explaining the purpose of your post.
- Include three or four important tips, organized into paragraphs.
- Give reasons for each tip and include examples or personal experience.
- Use linkers to add ideas.

WRITING PRACTICE

WRITING: Writing a magazine article

How to get a promotion

1 You may have been in your job for a couple of years, or maybe for only a few months, but you know you have more to offer your company and you want to aim higher. How do you persuade your boss to give you <u>a promotion</u>?

2 _____

First, look around you. Is there an obvious next step? You won't be promoted if there isn't a job to promote you to, so if <u>the job</u> doesn't exist, think about whether you can create it. Do you have <u>experience</u> or knowledge that isn't being used? Could your department be organized in a different way?

3 _____

The people in your company need to know how good you are. If you finish a piece of work early, tell your boss. If a client praises you, tell your boss. Remember that even <u>the hardworking</u> don't get what they deserve if nobody notices what they've achieved. Just make sure you don't annoy your colleagues – after all, they may be working for you soon!

4 _____

Someone needs to visit a client in <u>Baltimore</u> at the weekend. Someone needs to update the company website once <u>a week</u>. Why not offer? If your company realizes you are willing to work hard and do the things other people don't want to do, they won't want to lose you and that will put you in a strong position when you ask for that promotion.

5 There's nothing wrong with wanting to have a good career. <u>People</u> who stay at the same level often get bored with their jobs and don't do them very well. It's good to have a challenge, so if you feel you're ready for a promotion, go for it!

1 Read the article and choose the best headings for paragraphs 2–4.

Paragraph 2:
a Get a new skill   b Find the job you want   c Read the job adverts

Paragraph 3:
a Get yourself noticed   b Be better than your colleagues   c You are better than your boss

Paragraph 4:
a Do something different   b Fight for what you want   c Make yourself useful

2 Look at the <u>underlined</u> uses of *a/an*, *the* or (–) in the article. Now complete the gaps in the sentences below with *a/an*, *the* or (–).

1 Try not to arrange _____ meetings for the end of the day.
2 _____ California has a lot of high-tech companies.
3 Don't check your emails more than twice _____ day.
4 Make sure you have _____ clear reason for having a meeting.
5 Try to leave _____ office early on Fridays.
6 Only _____ lonely enjoy working at the weekends.
7 People like their colleagues to show _____ enthusiasm.
8 If you work in _____ open-plan office, don't speak loudly on the phone.

3 Write an article about one of the topics below.

What makes a good colleague?   *How to have effective meetings*   *Keeping a good work-life balance*

- Give your article an interesting title.
- Introduce the topic in an opening paragraph that readers can relate to.
- Develop your ideas in two or three paragraphs and give each one a heading.
- Summarize your ideas in the final paragraph.
- Pay attention to your use of definite and indefinite articles.

WRITING PRACTICE

WRITING: Writing a personal recommendation

Dear Mr Swain

This letter is to recommend Lara Manning as a house sitter while you are working abroad for two months. I first met Lara when she came to me for piano lessons in 2012. I taught her for four years and we have kept in touch since she left to go to music college where, as you may know, she is studying modern classical music.

Lara was a quiet, serious student, and one of the most talented musicians I have ever taught. From the age of 15, she started to babysit for my own children on Saturdays while I was teaching. She was a sensible, friendly babysitter and, despite being a little shy, she was also great fun: she loved running around playing games with the children. They enjoyed being with her and I was confident that they were safe and were being well looked after.

Lara has told me that you have a large vegetable garden. I know that Lara enjoys gardening, and she has helped her parents a lot with their garden. In addition, I am certain that she is an honest person, something that is essential for a house sitter. She has fed our cat on several occasions while we have been on holiday, and I have been very happy to let her have the keys to our house.

Lara is a charming young woman, who I'm sure will treat your home with respect. I would not hesitate to recommend her, but if you have any questions, please feel free to email me.

Yours sincerely

Jeannie Evans

1 Read Jeannie Evans's personal recommendation. Underline the places where she:

1. says what kind of person Lara is.
2. says how Mr Swain can get in touch with her.
3. gives specific examples of Lara's personal qualities.
4. explains how she knows Lara.

2 Find four pairs of adjectives in the personal recommendation above. Now match the two parts of the sentences and add commas after the first adjectives where necessary.

1. He knows how to look after valuable _____
2. She is a positive _____
3. He decided to move because of the difficult _____
4. My father has always had stressful _____
5. He has excellent _____

a. confident person.
b. demanding jobs.
c. interpersonal skills.
d. antique furniture.
e. political situation.

3 Imagine you are writing a personal recommendation. Use your own ideas to write about a quality that fits the example that follows.

1. _____
He travelled through Africa alone when he was only 18.

2. _____
He sat with the elderly patients all afternoon and made sure they had everything they needed.

3. _____
He spent all day checking the document and discovered several errors in it. He then explained the errors very politely to the author.

4. _____
He designed our student magazine and took all the photographs for it.

4 Think of someone you know who would be a good house sitter. Write a personal recommendation.

- Explain how you know the person.
- Describe his/her personal qualities and give examples.
- Offer to provide more information.
- Include at least three pairs of adjectives of opinion and fact and make sure they are in the correct order.

58 St Aldates
Oxford
OX1 1ST
United Kingdom

ISBN: 978-84-668-2102-5
CP: 642673
DL: M-42307-2018

© Richmond / Santillana Global S.L. 2019

Publishing Director: Deborah Tricker
Publisher: Luke Baxter
Editor: Peter Anderson
Proofreader: Emily Ashmore, Rachael Williamson
Design Manager: Lorna Heaslip
Cover Design: Richmond
Design & Layout: Lorna Heaslip, Jackie Hill at 320 Design Ltd.
Photo Researcher: Magdalena Mayo
Audio production: Tom, Dick and Debbie

Photos:
123RF; ALAMY/Arco Images GmbH, Oliver Knight, Elizabeth Whiting & Associates, Moviestore collection Ltd; GETTY IMAGES SALES SPAIN/Sturti, Bloomberg, Serts, Alex Wong, Filadendron, Yuri_Arcurs, DGLimages, LEON NEAL, PhotoAlto, Erierika, Thinkstock, Ronniechua, Diane39, Piotr Marcinski/EyeEm, Hero Images, Sam Edwards, Scott Olson, Emir Memedovski, Boston Globe, Ethan Miller, Image Source, bymuratdeniz, Inti St Clair, Martinedoucet, Antnio Guillem, PhotoQuest, ClarkandCompany, Rindoff/Dufour, Photos.com Plus, Dreet Production, TheCrimsonMonkey, valentinrussanov, Caiaimage/Sam Edwards, Sdominick, Tetra Images-Rob Lewine, Highwaystarz-Photography, Future Publishing/Olly Curtis, Alvarez; ISTOCKPHOTO/Getty Images Sales Spain; SPACEX; ARCHIVO SANTILLANA

Cover Photo: GETTY IMAGES SALES SPAIN/Martin Dimitrov

Impressão e Acabamento:
Log&Print Gráfica, Dados Variáveis e Logística S.A.
Lote: 796386
Código: 290521025

All rights reserved. No part of this book may be reproduced, stored in a retrieval system or transmitted in any form by any means, electronic, mechanical, photocopying, recording or otherwise, without the prior permission in writing of the Publisher.

We would like to thank the following reviewers for their valuable feedback which has made Personal Best possible. We extend our thanks to the many teachers and students not mentioned here.
Brad Bawtinheimer, Manuel Hidalgo, Paulo Dantas, Diana Bermúdez, Laura Gutiérrez, Hardy Griffin, Angi Conti, Christopher Morabito, Hande Kokce, Jorge Lobato, Leonardo Mercato, Mercilinda Ortiz, Wendy López

The Publisher has made every effort to trace the owner of copyright material; however, the Publisher will correct any involuntary omission at the earliest opportunity.

Printed in Brazil by